Upstream

ELEMENTARY

WORKBOOK

Student's Book

Virginia Evans - Jenny Dooley

Express Publishing

Published by Express Publishing

Liberty House, New Greenham Park, Newbury,
Berkshire RG19 6HW
Tel.: (0044) 1635 817 363
Fax: (0044) 1635 817 463
e-mail: inquiries@expresspublishing.co.uk
http://www.expresspublishing.co.uk

© Virginia Evans – Jenny Dooley, 2005

Design and Illustration © Express Publishing, 2005

Colour Illustrations: Stone

First published 2005
Second impression 2006

This book is not meant to be changed in any way.

Made in EU

ISBN-13: 978-1-84558-758-1
ISBN-10: 1-84558-758-8

Acknowledgements

Authors' Acknowledgements

We would like to thank all the staff at Express Publishing who have contributed their skills to producing this book. Thanks for their support and patience are due in particular to: Meryl Philips (Editor in Chief), Julie Rich (senior editor); Nina Peters (editorial assistant); Alex Barton (senior production controller) and the Express Publishing design team; and Emily Newton, Kevin Harris, Daniel Parker, Erica Thompson and Timothy Forster. We would also like to thank those institutions and teachers who piloted the manuscript, and whose comments and feedback were invaluable in the production of the book.

While every effort has been made to trace all the copyright holders, if any have been inadvertently overlooked the publishers will be pleased to make the necessary arrangements at the first opportunity.

Contents

Vocabulary Practice

1 a. What job does each person do? Label the pictures.

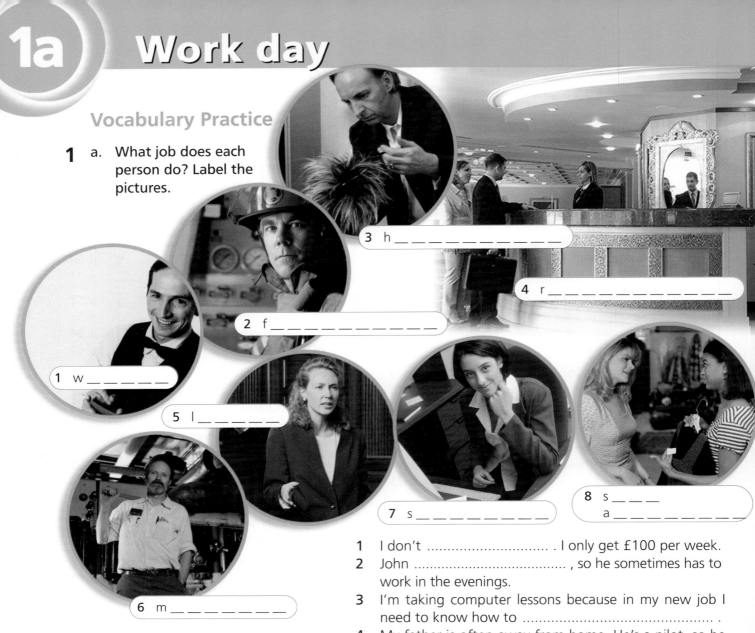

1 w _ _ _ _ _ _

2 f _ _ _ _ _ _ _ _ _ _ _

3 h _ _ _ _ _ _ _ _ _ _ _ _

4 r _ _ _ _ _ _ _ _ _ _ _ _ _ _

5 l _ _ _ _ _ _ _

6 m _ _ _ _ _ _ _ _

7 s _ _ _ _ _ _ _ _ _ _

8 s _ _ _ _
a _ _ _ _ _ _ _ _ _ _

b. Use the adjectives below to make sentences about the jobs in Ex. 1a.

- physically fit • brave
- friendly • polite • patient
- reliable • creative

A waiter needs to be polite and friendly with his/her customers.

2 Match the words in the two columns to make phrases. Use them in their correct form to complete the sentences.

1	work	a	a uniform
2	get	b	part-time
3	use	c	a lot
4	travel	d	shifts
5	wear	e	a computer
		f	indoors
		g	9 to 5
		h	paid a lot

1 I don't .... I only get £100 per week.
2 John .... , so he sometimes has to work in the evenings.
3 I'm taking computer lessons because in my new job I need to know how to ....
4 My father is often away from home. He's a pilot, so he ....
5 He .... as a waiter, but he wants to find a full-time job.

Listening

3 🎧 Listen to the radio advert about a careers fair and fill in the gaps (1-5).

Travel and Tourism

Careers Fair, (0) *Liverpool*

May 26th to (1) ....
- Thousands of **(2)** .... vacancies
- Representatives from international tour companies, travel agencies and airlines

Where? St. George's Hall (opposite Lime Street **(3)** ....).
Opening times: (4) .... to 6pm
For more information please call 0151 578 **(5)** ....

Home   Message Board   Games   Music   Cool Sites   Jokes

TeenSpot !

The website for teens ...

Teens Speak Out!

THIS WEEK'S TOPIC:

Do you help out at home?
How do you feel about it?

Darren, 17, Lincoln
I help quite a lot actually, especially at weekends. I sometimes mow the lawn, for example, wash the car or dust the furniture. My mum and dad both work really hard all week, so I think they need a bit of help.

Stacey, 16, London
I sometimes help my mum after school. I often take out the rubbish or wash the dishes. It's not fair though! My brother never helps! He just disappears into his bedroom and lets me do all the work!

Greg, 18, Manchester
To be honest, I don't usually help much with the housework, I just clean my own bedroom once a week. At the moment I'm doing exams. It's not that I don't want to help, it's just that I never find the time!

Jenny, 18, Scarborough
My mum and dad run a hotel. They are really busy, so I often help to make the beds, cook the breakfast or dust the furniture. I don't mind at all. Sometimes my parents even pay me!

Vocabulary Practice

1 **a.** **Match the words/phrases in column A with those in column B.**

A		B	
1	make	a	the beds
2	meet	b	the furniture
3	take out	c	in the gym
4	mow	d	my friends
5	dust	e	the clothes
6	do	f	the rubbish
7	iron	g	the lawn
8	work out	h	the washing up

b. **Use some of the phrases above to complete the sentences below.**

1 The garden is a mess. Can you ....
...., please?
2 The bin smells really bad. Please ....
....
3 You are looking really fit. Do you ....
...................................?
4 I usually ....on Saturdays. We go for pizza.

Reading

2 **Do you sometimes help with household chores? What do you do? How often?**

3 **a.** **Look at the text. What is it? What do you expect to read? Read and check.**

b. **Read again and mark the statements R (right), W (wrong) or DS (doesn't say).**

1 Darren and Jenny both help because their parents have a lot to do. ....
2 Stacey is annoyed with her brother. ....
3 Greg doesn't want to help with the housework. ....
4 Jenny's parents make gourmet meals at the hotel. ....

4 **Write your own comment for the message board.**

Everyday English

5 **Choose the correct response.**

1 A: Can you please vacuum the floor?
   B: a Yes, I do.
      b Yes, sure.

2 A: Would you mind walking the dog this evening?
   B: a No, I'm not.
      b I'm afraid I can't.

3 A: Do you think you could do the washing up?
   B: a Sorry, I can't.
      b Sorry, I couldn't.

4 A: Could you iron the clothes, please?
   B: a No problem.
      b Sometimes.

1 There were 300 people at the ....
2 Joan is her .... They tell each other everything.
3 I'm too tired to go out. We can .... if you want.
4 She .... at the company's annual party every year.

Vocabulary Practice

1 Choose the activity that matches each picture.

1 They are **going swimming/visiting relatives**.
2 Mary and Janet are **going dancing/going shopping**.
3 They are **cooking for friends/having dinner**.
4 They are **going camping/having a picnic**.
5 Susan and Tim are **relaxing at home/going to the cinema**.
6 They are **eating out/having a barbecue**.

2 Choose a picture and describe it to your partner. Talk about: place - weather - people - clothes - activities - feelings.

3 Underline the character adjectives, then match the two halves of the sentences.

1 Emma is always the life and soul of the party.
2 John is really popular.
3 Sarah's a bit quiet tonight.
4 Simon's so lazy!
5 Your friend doesn't say much, does she?
6 Are you getting on well with your new neighbour?

a Yes, everyone likes him.
b He's really friendly.
c He never helps with the housework.
d He's got so many friends!
e Oh, don't worry, she's just a bit shy.
f Is she ok? I think she's really tired.
g She's so outgoing!

1 ..... 2 ..... 3 ..... 4 ..... 5 ..... 6 .....

4 Match the words. Use the phrases to complete the sentences.

1 wedding
2 rent
3 close
4 meet

A new people
B a video
C friends
D reception

Everyday English

5 Complete the dialogue with phrases from the list.

- Why don't
- Would you like to
- Great idea!
- I'm afraid I can't
- Let's meet
- how about going

A: Richie, **1)** .... to the cinema tonight?
B: Tonight? **2)** ....
A: Why not?
B: I have a class until eight.
A: That's ok. **3)** .... we meet after your class and go to the cinema at nine?
B: That's a good idea.
A: **4)** .... at eight twenty at the square. **5)** .... get a quick bite before the cinema?
B: **6)** ....! I'm always hungry after my class!

Speaking

6 Work in pairs. It's Saturday morning and you are talking to your friend trying to arrange something for the afternoon. Use the notes to discuss.

- make a suggestion
- respond negatively & give reasons
- suggest sth else

A letter to a pen friend

1 Read the rubric and answer the questions.

> This is part of a letter you received from your pen friend.
>
> *In your next letter, please tell me how you spend your weekends. What do you like doing?*
>
> Write a letter to your pen friend.

1 What are you going to write?
2 Who is going to read it?
3 What words/phrases related to the theme can you think of?
4 How would you start/end a letter to a pen friend?

2 Read the letter and match the paragraphs to the headings.

a opening remarks/reason for writing
b closing remarks/ask friend to write back
c weekend activities

Dear Antonio,

[1] *How's everything? I hope you are fine. Here's what I do in my free time.*

[2] *I spend my week working hard at college, but my weekends are pretty busy too. On Saturday mornings, I work part-time as a sales assistant at the local supermarket, then I meet my friends for a burger and a Coke. In the afternoon, I usually play football, but I sometimes go swimming at the sports centre. On Saturday nights, I'm usually tired, so I stay at home. I often rent a video or play on my computer. On Sundays, I do my college work and send emails or write letters. I usually get an early night.*

[3] *Well, that's all, I guess. Write soon and tell me what you like to do in your free time.*

Best wishes,
Simon

Joining sentences

3 a. Read the letter and circle five words which join sentences.

b. Join the sentences with one of the circled words.

1 I go to the cinema. I go to a café.
   *I go to the cinema, **then** I go to a café.*
2 I usually play football. Sometimes, I go diving.
3 I often play computer games. I surf the Net.
4 I'm too tired to cook during the week. I order out.
5 I visit my friend. We have lunch together.

Opening/Closing remarks

4 Which of the following sentences can you use in the first/last paragraph?

- Hi! How are you? ....
- Write again soon. ....
- I can't wait to hear all your news. ....
- Thanks so much for your letter. ....
- How's it going? ....
- I'd better go now. ....

Your turn

5 Which of the following do you do at the weekend? Discuss with a partner.

- meet friends • play sports
- work • have lessons
- go shopping • watch TV
- go to the cinema
- go to bed/get up late • other

6 Write a letter to a pen friend telling him/her what you do at the weekend. Use your answers from Ex. 5 to help you. You can use the letter in Ex. 2 as a model.

Present Simple

1 a. Look at the table, then write as in the example.

	Charlie	Karen
live in Manchester?	✗	✓
have a pet?	✓	✗
speak Spanish?	✗	✓
play football?	✓	✗
work at a hospital?	✗	✗

1   *Does Charlie live in Manchester?*
    No, ... He lives in London.
2   ....?
    Yes, ... He has a dog.
3   ....?
    Yes, ... She is Spanish.
4   ....?
    No, ... She plays tennis.
5   ....?
    No, ... She works in an office.

b. Look at the table and complete the sentences.

1   Karen *lives* in Manchester.
2   Karen .... a pet.
3   Charlie .... Spanish.
4   Karen .... football.
5   Charlie and Karen ....
    at a hospital.

2 Put the verbs in brackets into the correct present simple form.

1   A: What job ....
       (your father/do)?
    B: He's a mechanic. He ...... (love) his job.
2   A: .... (you/find) your job tiring?
    B: Sometimes, when I .... (work)
       long hours.
3   A: ....
       (Pete/have) a good job?
    B: Well, he .... (earn) a lot!
4   A: ....
       (you/know) how to use a computer?
    B: Well, I .... (surf) the Net quite
       often but my sister ....
       (not/like) it at all.
5   A: .... (Mike/ride) his
       bike to school?
    B: No, he .... (catch) the bus.
6   A: .... (your dog/bite)?
    B: No, he .... He ...... (be) very quiet.

3 Use the prompts to make questions. Then, answer them about yourself.

1   your father/work in an office?
    Does your father work in an office?
    Yes, he does./No, he doesn't. He is a teacher.
2   you/want to be a doctor?
3   your friend/study at university?
4   your parents/travel a lot?
5   your mother/work long hours?
6   you/work part-time?
7   your teacher/give lots of tests?

4 a. Fill in: *never, usually, sometimes*.

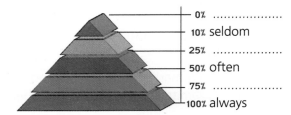

0%	....
10%	seldom
25%	....
50%	often
75%	....
100%	always

b. Use adverbs of frequency and the phrases to ask and answer.

How often do you ...
• vacuum your bedroom?
• cook dinner for the family?
• meet your friends?
• get up early?

5 Fill in: *does, is*.

A: This **1)** .... my cousin, Mary.
B: What **2)** .... she do?
A: She **3)** .... a teacher.
B: Where **4)** .... she come from?
A: She comes from France.
B: How old **5)** .... she?
A: She **6)** .... twenty-nine.
B: **7)** .... she married?
A: No, she **8)** .... single.

6 Put the words in the correct order.

1   you/today/beach/the/going/to/are?
    ....
2   tomorrow/Steve/fishing/not/is/going.
    ....
3   Peter/chess/are/David/playing/and/now.
    ....
4   Samantha/what/is/eating/now?
    ....
5   tonight/Sally/having/is/a/party.
    ....

7 Read John's agenda. Ask and answer questions, as in the example.

	Monday	Tuesday
10 am	attend drama class	have guitar lesson
1 pm	go to the bank	
3 pm		play chess with Jack
5 pm		
8 pm	watch football game	meet Karen for dinner

1 attend/drama/class/Tuesday/10 am?
A: Is John attending drama class on Tuesday at 10 am?
B: No, he isn't. He is attending drama class on Monday at 10 am.
2 go/to/bank/Tuesday/1 pm?
3 play/chess/with Jack/Monday/3 pm?
4 watch/football game/on/Tuesday/8 pm?
5 meet/Karen/for dinner/Monday/8 pm?

8 Answer the questions about yourself.

1 Are you making a sandwich?
No, I'm not. I'm reading a book.
2 Is your mother preparing dinner?
3 Are you going out tonight?
4 Are you learning to play the piano?
5 Is your sister having a birthday party on Saturday?
6 Are you studying hard these days?
7 Is your father going to London tomorrow?

9 Put the verbs in brackets into the *present simple* or *present continuous*.

1 A: Where's Paul?
B: In his room. He .... **(do)** his homework.
2 A: What time .... **(you/start)** work every morning?
B 9 o'clock.
3 A: Where .... **(you/go)**?
B: I .... **(go)** to the supermarket.
4 A: How often .... **(you/drink)** tea?
B: Twice a day.
5 A: What .... **(Peter/do)**?
B: He .... **(have)** a shower at the moment.
6 A: Tom is very busy.
B: Yes. He .... **(work)** very hard these days.

7 A: Why .... **(you/pack)** your suitcase?
B: Because I .... **(travel)** to Rome tomorrow.
8 A: What time .... **(the film/start)**?
B: It .... **(start)** at 7 o'clock.
9 A: Do you like basketball?
B: Yes, but I .... **(prefer)** football.
10 A: Jane looks very fit.
B: Yes. She .... **(exercise)** a lot at the moment.

10 Lynn has made some promises to herself. Use the phrases to write sentences.

• join a gym • practise the violin
• save some money • eat more vegetables
• take a computer course

Lynn is going to join a gym.

11 Look at the pictures. What are they going to do? Write sentences, as in the example.

• dive • blow out the candles • play tennis
• buy flowers • try on a dress • have lunch

He's going to blow out the candles.

Leisure Activities in Britain

Britain's most common leisure activities are **home-based** or **social**. Watching television and videos, and listening **1)** .... the radio are the most popular leisure pastimes. Britain's **regular weekly** dramas or 'soap operas' such **2)** .... *EastEnders* and *Coronation Street* have more **viewers** than any other programme. Listening to music is **3)** .... a popular pastime. Pop and rock albums **4)** .... the most common type of music the British buy, and pop is their **5)** .... type of music.

The most common free-time activity outside the home among adults is a visit to the pub. **6)** .... popular leisure activities **include** visits to the theatre or cinema. There **7)** .... over 1,500 cinemas in Britain, and 300 theatres, of which about 100 are in London. Britain's most famous **theatre company**,

The Royal Shakespeare Company, performs both in Stratford-upon-Avon, Shakespeare's birthplace, and in London.

Of all sporting activities, walking is the most popular **8)** .... men and women of all ages. While men enjoy golf, snooker and football, women prefer swimming, keep-fit classes and yoga.

1	A of	B to	C at
2	A as	B of	C that
3	A and	B too	C also
4	A are	B have	C can
5	A favourite	B like	C nice
6	A The	B Other	C Some
7	A play	B are	C have
8	A with	B for	C of

1 Look at the pictures. How do you think the British spend their free time? Read through the text and check.

2 Read the text and choose the correct word to fill in the gaps. Listen and check. Then explain the words in bold.

3 Read again, then make notes about Britain's most common leisure activities. Use your notes to tell the class.

4 Which are the most common leisure activities in your country? Compare them to Britain's.

Progress Check

Vocabulary & Grammar

A Circle the correct item.

1 If you want to be a firefighter, you have to be ....
   A polite   B brave   C creative

2 I .... get up early in the morning. I am never late for school.
   A always   B sometimes C rarely

3 She .... to work every day.
   A is driving B is going to drive
   C drives

4 They are .... their dinner at the moment. They are enjoying it.
   A having   B doing   C catching

5 How often do you .... the lawn?
   A mow   B walk   C dust

6 Sheila is going to visit her grandmother .... Sunday.
   A on   B at   C in

7 Would you mind .... the dog, please?
   A walk   B walking   C to walk

8 He works in an office. He is a ....
   A waiter   B bus driver
   C graphic designer

9 Fiona and Jim .... out tonight.
   A eat   B going to eat C are eating

10 Why don't we .... a barbecue on Sunday?
   A have   B do   C cook

11 Can you please .... the furniture in the living room?
   A dust   B mow   C vacuum

12 What .... tomorrow evening?
   A do you   B do you do
   C are you doing

13 How about ..... camping at the weekend?
   A going   B having   C doing

14 Working with children is very ....
   A dangerous B relaxing   C rewarding

15 He is a nurse so he has to work ....
   A part time   B shifts   C outdoors

16 Does she work long hours? No, she ....
   A aren't   B isn't   C doesn't

17 Teachers need to be .... with students.
   A patient   B brave   C reliable

18 We are all going .... a picnic at the weekend.
   A with   B on   C at

19 He enjoys .... out at the gym.
   A getting   B catching   C working

20 Can you please .... the window? It's very hot.
   A open   B opening   C to open

$$\left(\begin{matrix} \text{Marks:} & \text{——} \\ 20 \times 3 & 60 \end{matrix} \right)$$

Everyday English

B Complete the exchanges.

- That's a good idea
- Do you think you could
- How about
- Shall we
- Would you mind

1 A: Why don't we go to the cinema this evening?
   B: ....

2 A: .... vacuuming the floor, please?
   B: No problem.

3 A: .... going jogging tomorrow morning at dawn?
   B: I'm afraid I can't.

4 A: .... have a picnic at the weekend?
   B: Sure! Why not?

5 A: .... make the beds, please?
   B: Sorry, I can't. I'm busy.

$$\left(\begin{matrix} \text{Marks:} & \text{——} \\ 5 \times 8 & 40 \end{matrix} \right)$$

$$\left(\begin{matrix} \text{Total:} & \text{————} \\ & \text{100 marks} \end{matrix} \right)$$

11

Vocabulary Practice

1 Read the sentences and fill in the correct word.

1 When you feel sad and upset because of a difficult situation you are d *epressed*.

2 The opposite of optimistic is p _ _ _ _ _ _ _ _ _ _.

3 When you don't know what's happening or don't know what to do, you feel c _ _ _ _ _ _ _.

4 When you are looking forward to something you are e _ _ _ _ _ _.

5 When you are unhappy because you are alone you are l _ _ _ _ _.

6 If you are not worried, scared or angry, you feel c _ _ _.

2 Use the prompts to make sentences about each person.

 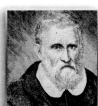  

Johann Sebastian Bach
Germany
1685-1750

Marco Polo
Italy
1254-1324

Isaac Newton
England
1642-1727

Marilyn Monroe
America
1926-1962

1 *Johann Sebastian Bach was a German composer.*

2 ....

3 ....

4 ....

3 Complete the phrases with words from the list. Use some of the phrases to complete the sentences (1-4).

• public • early • compose • fall • lose • learn

a .... age
b .... the violin
c .... music
d .... in love
e .... hearing
f .... performance

1 He gave his first .... when he was nine years old.

2 Beethoven .... but was still able to .... great ....

3 It's best to learn an instrument at an ....
.... rather than when you are older.

4 They .... as soon as they saw each other and got married within a month!

Everyday English
(Asking for/Giving personal information)

4 Read the questions and fill in the answers. Then, write similar questions and answers for two more of the famous people from Ex. 2.

A: Who was Marco Polo?
B: **1)** *He was a famous explorer.*
A: When was he born?
B: **2)** ....
A: Where was he born?
B: **3)** ....
A: What nationality was he?
B: **4)** ....
A: When did he die?
B: **5)** ....

Listening

5 🎧 Listen and match the students (1-5) to the famous people (A-H).

Students

[1] Philip
[2] Tom
[3] Joshua
[4] Melanie
[5] Jayne

Famous People

A crime writers
B American presidents
C Hollywood actors
D explorers
E jazz musicians
F sports personalities
G ballet dancers
H TV presenters

Vocabulary Practice

1 Underline the correct word or phrase.

1 They are **riding horses/fighting**.
2 He is holding **an axe/a spear**.
3 He is **wearing armour/holding a flag**.
4 They are **attacking/watching a re-enactment**.

Reading

2 a. Look at the pictures and headings in the advert. What do you think you can do/see at the museum? Read and check.

b. Read again and choose the best word for each gap (1-5). Then, explain the words in bold.

0	Ⓐ is	B are	C were
1	A It	B We	C They
2	A from	B of	C for
3	A every	B any	C all
4	A including	B include	C includes
5	A for	B to	C of

Everyday English
(Talking about a past experience)

3 Circle the correct response.

1 A: How was your summer?
   B: **a** I had a great time.
     b It's ok, thanks.

2 A: How did you spend your weekend?
   B: **a** Oh, it's amazing!
     b I stayed at home.

3 A: What did you do last night?
   B: **a** Nothing special.
     b I didn't watch TV.

4 A: I got married last week.
   B: **a** You're kidding!
     b You've got to see it.

5 A: I went on holiday to Thailand.
   B: **a** Well, nothing special.
     b What was it like?

Museum of
Childhood

The Museum of Childhood **0)** *is* part of the Victoria and Albert Museum in London. **1)** .... first opened in 1872 and has one of the largest and oldest collections of children's toys, including **dolls, teddy bears, train sets, rocking horses, board games** and some **2)** .... the first **jigsaw puzzles** ever made!

Activities
We have daily activities for children of **3)** .... ages, including art activities and **interactive story-telling**.

Exhibitions
Recent exhibitions **4)** .... a **vegetable patch** made by a local after-school club out of everyday objects, a **sculpture** of seaside **memories** and a display of photographs showing the lives of different children across London.

Schools
We organise interactive sessions where pupils have the chance **5)** .... hear about and play with toys from the past.

Vocabulary Practice

1 Read the definitions and match them to the words.

A [ ] terraced
B [ ] cottage
C [ ] studio
D [ ] detached

E [ ] semi-detached
F [ ] mansion
G [ ] castle
H [ ] bungalow

1 A very large, expensive house.
2 A small house that you usually find in the countryside.
3 A modern flat for one or two people with the kitchen, the living room and the bedroom in one large room, and a separate bathroom.
4 A house that is not connected to any other building.
5 A house that is connected to a similar house on one side only.
6 A very large and very old building where a lot of people used to live.
7 A row of small houses that are connected to one another.
8 A house that has only one floor.

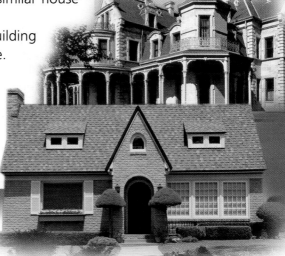

Speaking

4 In pairs, look at the advertisement and use the prompts to ask and answer questions.

- Where? • Cost? • Number/rooms?
- Garden? • Telephone number?

2 Circle the odd one out.

1 bedroom, attic, fence, living room
2 towels, pillows, mirror, shower
3 cupboard, rug, chest of drawers, wardrobe
4 fridge, cooker, kitchen, four-poster bed
5 porch, balcony, garden, staircase
6 detached, manor, terraced, room

3 Complete the opposites. Then, use the adjectives to write sentences about the houses in Ex. 1.

1 small ≠ s__ __ __ __ __ __ __
2 traditional ≠ m__ __ __ __ __
3 cheap ≠ e__ __ __ __ __ __ __ __
4 ugly ≠ a__ __ __ __ __ __ __ __ __
5 decorated ≠ p__ __ __ __

FOR SALE

Five-bedroom house close to the centre of London.

Beautiful family house, five minutes from the centre!

- Bright and large living room
- Dining room
- Kitchen
- Five bedrooms
- Three bathrooms
- Large garden

£ 600,000

Contact: 0967 987 4576
Email:
greathouses@sales.com

An article about a famous person

1 a. Read the title and the introduction to the article. Who was Audrey Hepburn?

b. What kind of information do you expect to find in the rest of the article? Read and check.

2 a. Read again. Which paragraph: *a) describes her early years? b) describes her later years? c) says who she was? d) says what people thought of her/gives a short conclusion?*

Audrey Hepburn was a beautiful, <u>stylish</u> Hollywood star. In 1996, the British magazine *Harpers & Queen* named her 'The Most <u>Fascinating</u> Woman of our Time'.

Audrey was born in Brussels, Belgium, on 4ᵗʰ May, 1929. Her father was a <u>wealthy</u> English banker and her mother was a Dutch baroness. After difficult times in Holland during World War II, Audrey went to a ballet school in London and later became a model. A film producer spotted her and she began to act in films.

Audrey became <u>famous</u> almost instantly in the USA when she won an Oscar for her role in the film *Roman Holiday* in 1953. She then gave other <u>brilliant</u> performances in popular films such as *Sabrina* (1954), *Breakfast at Tiffany's* (1961) and *My Fair Lady* (1964). In 1988, she began to work for the United Nations, helping children in Latin America and Africa until her death in 1993.

In total, Audrey Hepburn made 31 movies. Everyone loved her and she is an inspiration to us all. Hollywood will remember her for many years to come!

b. Circle the verbs in the article. Which tense is mainly used? Why?

c. Now look at the underlined words. Which of the words below could replace them? What kind of words are they?

- excellent - well-known - interesting - rich
- fashionable

3 In pairs, use the notes about Yuri Gagarin to ask and answer questions, as in the example.

A: *What was Yuri Gagarin famous for?*
B: *He was the first man in space.*

Yuri Gagarin

Famous for: first man in space
First words from space: "I see Earth. It's so beautiful!"
Date and place of birth: 9ᵗʰ March, 1934, near Moscow, Russia
Early years: grew up on farm; 1951: left school as a trained metalworker; 1955: joined Soviet Air Force; had natural talent for flying; volunteered to become cosmonaut
Later years: 12ᵗʰ April, 1961: travelled into space for 108 mins on Soviet spaceship, Vostok I; headline news all over the world
Death: 7ᵗʰ March, 1968, age 34, plane crash
Other Information: brave, energetic man, loved life; crater on Moon named after him; made his mark on history

Your turn

4 a. Read the rubric and underline the key words. How many paragraphs will your article have? What information will you include in each?

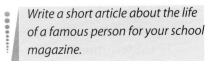

Write a short article about the life of a famous person for your school magazine.

b. Write your article, using the notes in Ex. 3 and appropriate tenses and adjectives. Use the article in Ex. 2 as a model.

Past Simple
(regular & irregular verbs)

1 Complete the fact file with the *past simple* form of the verbs in brackets.

Fact File

Claude Monet
(1840-1926)

- Monet **0)** *was* **(be)** born in Paris, France.
- He **1)** .... **(not/want)** to paint traditional art.
  He **2)** .... **(begin)** to paint in a new style of art, called Impressionism.
- He **3)** .... **(become)** well-known after he **4)** .... **(finish)** his painting *The Woman in the Green Dress* in 1866.
- Monet **5)** .... **(marry)** Camille Doncieux in 1873. They **6)** .... **(have)** two sons.
- Camille **7)** .... **(fall)** ill and **8)** .... **(die)** in 1879.
- Between 1883 and 1908, Monet **9)** .... **(travel)** to the Mediterranean and **10)** .... **(paint)** many beautiful landscapes and seascapes.
- He **11)** .... **(die)** in Giverny, France in 1926.

2 Use the prompts to write questions and answers, as in the example.

1 go to the gym last night? **(have coffee with friends)**
   A: Did you go to the gym last night?
   B: No, I didn't. I had coffee with friends.
2 see the news this morning? **(not switch on TV)**
3 John write that article? **(Sam write it)**
4 catch bus home yesterday? **(take Underground)**
5 do the shopping this afternoon? **(not have time)**
6 Mary get back from London today? **(come back yesterday)**

3 Read Bill's letter to his pen friend about his holiday and put the verbs in brackets in the *past simple*.

Dear Fred,
Sorry I **1)** .... **(not/write)** earlier but I just **2)** .... **(get)** back from my camping holiday. I **3)** .... **(go)** away with my parents and my cousins and we all **4)** .... **(have)** a really good time. We **5)** .... **(stay)** at a very beautiful campsite in the middle of a forest. We **6)** .... **(go)** hiking and exploring every day. The hills and countryside **7)** .... **(be)** truly beautiful. We **8)** .... **(swim)** in the river and I also **9)** .... **(learn)** how to fish. In the evening, we **10)** .... **(cook)** over the campfire, **11)** .... **(sing)** songs and **12)** .... **(tell)** stories. Luckily, it **13)** .... **(not/rain)** for the whole two weeks. I **14)** .... **(love)** every minute of it!
I look forward to hearing about your holiday, so write back soon.
Love,
Jeremiah

4 Write sentences about yourself using the time expressions below.

- last Christmas • last week • this morning
- two years ago • an hour ago
- the day before yesterday

....
....
....
....
....
....
....
....
....
....

Wh- questions

5 Use the information in the box and the prompts to write questions and answers, as in the example.

The Battle of Waterloo

- 18th June, 1815
- south of Brussels, Belgium
- 11 am-10 pm
- around 150,000 soldiers
- The Duke of Wellington and his allies defeated Napoleon Bonaparte
- 50,000 men dead

1 When/take place?
2 Where/take place?
3 How long/last?
4 Who/take part?
5 What happen/in the end?
6 How many men/die?

A: When did the battle of Waterloo take place?
B: It took place …

6 Ask questions where the underlined word is the answer.

1 <u>Sally</u> called Stewart a few minutes ago.
Who called Stewart a few minutes ago?
2 We visited <u>an old castle</u> on Saturday.
....
3 John and Tracy bought <u>two</u> little puppies.
....
....
4 I went <u>to Portugal</u> for my holidays last year.
....
....
5 They chose the <u>red</u> sofa for their new living room.
....
....
6 The accident happened <u>on Thursday</u>.
....
7 We travelled to the airport <u>by train</u>.
....

Used to

7 Fill in the gaps with *used to* in the correct form and the verb in brackets.

A: Grandma, what **1)** *did you use to do* **(you/do)** for fun when you were young?
B: Well, we **2)** .... **(not/watch TV)** because we didn't have one in those days. We **3)** .... **(play)** outside a lot and we **4)** .... **(go)** for long walks in the countryside.
A: **5)** .... **(you/listen)** to the radio?
B: Yes, we did and we **6)** .... **(read)** books and play card games, too.
A: Which was your favourite?
B: I **7)** .... **(love)** playing 'Old Maid'. I can teach you how to play it if you want.

8 Mrs Forbes retired and moved to the south of France. Her life is very different now. Use the prompts to ask and answer questions as in the example.

THEN	NOW
Live in a town	Live in a village
Drive a car	Ride a bicycle
Wear warm clothes	Wear light clothes
Eat a lot of meat	Eat a lot of cheese
Wake up early	Wake up late

A: Did Mrs Forbes use to live in a village?
B: No, she didn't. She used to live in a town.

Used to vs Past Simple

9 Use the prompts to write sentences using the *past simple* or the *used to* form where possible.

1 Mr Smith/live/in Paris/when he/be/young
Mr Smith lived/used to live in Paris when he was young.
2 I/watch/an amazing film last night
....
3 We/not have/computers/when we/be/ little
....
4 Dave/get married/two years ago
....
5 Kate and Laura/not be/friends at school
....
6 Matt/play/hockey at university
....

1 Who was King Arthur? How do you think the pictures below are related to him? Read and check.

GUINEVERE · MERLIN · UTHER · LANCELOT · EXCALIBUR

2 a. Read again and answer the following questions. Then, explain the words in bold.

1 Why did Merlin take Arthur away?

2 How did Arthur become king?

3 Why did Arthur sentence his wife to death?

4 How did Arthur die?

b. Make up a sentence which best describes the picture from the story.

King Arthur

A A very long time ago there was an English king called Uther Pendragon. He married a woman called Lady Igraine and they had a son, Arthur. King Uther had lots of **enemies**, so Merlin, a magician, took Arthur away and gave him to a friend to **look after**. The friend never told Arthur that his father was the King of England.

B When King Uther died, Merlin called all the Lords together. He told them that the person who could **pull** the magical **sword**, Excalibur, from the stone it was in, would be the next king of England. The only man able to pull the sword out was Arthur, so he became the new king.

C Arthur was a good king. When he married Lady Guinevere, her father gave him the famous Round Table as a **wedding gift**. Arthur **ruled** England with the help of his brave knights. One of them, Sir Lancelot, **fell in love** with Guinevere. When Arthur **found out** about it he **sentenced** Guinevere to death. Lancelot **saved** Guinevere and they **ran away** together.

D King Arthur was very angry and **chased** after them. While he was away he left his **nephew**, Mordred, **in charge of** the **kingdom**. Mordred tried to **take over**, though, and Arthur returned to stop him. There was a huge **battle** and both Mordred and Arthur died. When Guinevere heard what had happened she went to France and became a **nun**. Lancelot spent the rest of his life **alone**.

3 Make notes under the headings. Use your notes to tell the class about King Arthur.

- family background • early years
- later years (wedding) • death

4 Is there a popular legend in your country? Tell the class.

Progress Check

Vocabulary & Grammar

A Circle the correct item.

1 They have very little furniture; their house is very ....
   A traditional   B plain   C decorated

2 Marie .... the train to work this morning.
   A catch   B catches   C caught

3 The knight pulled out his .... and ran onto the battlefield.
   A sword   B shield   C armour

4 Your clean trousers are hanging in the ....
   A cupboard   B attic   C wardrobe

5 Who did .... to your birthday party?
   A you invited   B you invite
   C invited you

6 You can see old steam .... in this museum.
   A paintings   B jewellery   C engines

7 Helen didn't .... with us last night.
   A come   B came   C comes

8 I don't understand this; I'm very ....
   A depressed   B cheerful   C confused

9 Did you switch off the .... when you finished making the omelette?
   A cooker   B fridge   C kitchen

10 He doesn't have many friends here; he must be ....
   A lonely   B optimistic   C pessimistic

11 The .... got ready for the battle.
   A soldiers   B flags   C horses

12 Who .... just now? – Peter. He wanted to ask me something.
   A did you call   B called you
   C you called

13 She lives in a nice little .... in the city centre.
   A studio   B cottage   C mansion

14 The army .... their enemy very early in the morning.
   A rode   B held   C attacked

15 Did .... to ride a bike to school when you were young?
   A you use   B you used   C used you

16 Look at the colours! I really like this ....'s work.
   A painter   B politician   C astronaut

17 This room is very ....; it can easily fit all our furniture.
   A modern   B spacious   C attractive

18 Columbus was the .... who discovered America.
   A writer   B scientist   C explorer

19 Lessons .... last week.
   A begin   B began   C begun

20 I didn't .... history at school.
   A use to like   B used to like   C liked

(Marks: ——)
(20x3   60)

Everyday English

B Circle the correct response.

1 A: How was your summer?
   B: **a** It was fantastic!
      b What about you?

2 A: What did you do at the weekend?
   B: **a** It was boring.
      b Nothing special.

3 A: When was Martha born?
   B: **a** In 1998.
      b In the USA.

4 A: Who was Audrey Hepburn?
   B: **a** She was born in 1929.
      b She was a famous actress.

5 A: How did you spend your holiday?
   B: **a** I went to England.
      b Last week.

(Marks: ——)
(5x8   40)

(Total: ——)
(100 marks)

19

3a Holiday time

Vocabulary Practice

1 Complete the words in the advertisment.

Visit Hawaii

Relax on white **1)** s__ __ __ __ beaches.
Eat **2)** l__ __ __ __ dishes.
Take part in cultural events with **3)** t__ __ __ __ __ __ __ __ __ __ costumes.
Try a wide range of **4)** w__ __ __ __ sports.
Stay in **5)** l__ __ __ __ __ __ __ 5-star hotels.
Take a tour of **6)** a__ __ __ __ __ __ ruins.
Buy **7)** h__ __ __ __ __ __ __ souvenirs.

2 Label the pictures with words from the box.

- white-water rafting • snorkelling
- windsurfing • jet skiing • horse riding
- fishing • water skiing • cliff diving

1 ....
2 ....
3 ....
4 ....
5 ....
6 ....
7 ....
8 ....

3 Underline the correct adjective.

1 The food at the restaurant was a little **busy/ spicy** but absolutely **delicious/luxurious**.
2 The beach in front of this **expensive/ colourful**, **sandy/family** hotel is very **clean/bright**.
3 They all wear **narrow/colourful** costumes for the parades.
4 We enjoyed our walk along the **cobbled/ quality** streets of the little village.

Listening

4 🎧 You will hear a conversation between a travel agent and someone who wants to book a holiday. For questions 1-5 choose *A, B* or *C*.

1 The travel agent suggests going to ....
   A the Canary Islands   B Italy
   C Greece

2 The holiday in Tenerife is for ....
   A 14 nights   B 7 nights   C 9 nights

3 The holiday costs ....
   A £360   B £306   C £316

4 There is no discount if your child is ....
   A over 11   B over 6   C over 5

5 The address of the travel agency is ....
   A 33 Liberty Avenue
   B 33 Queen's Road
   C 33 Walker Street

20

Vocabulary Practice

1 **a.** Match the verbs in column A to the phrases in column B.

A		B	
1	travel	a	a motorbike/bike
2	fly	b	your luggage with you
3	take	c	in a plane
4	ride	d	a car
5	hire	e	the wrong bus/train
6	use	f	clear of the doors
7	fasten	g	the gap
8	mind	h	your seatbelt
9	stand	i	on a cruise ship
10	keep	j	the Underground

b. Use some of the phrases in Ex. 1a to complete the sentences below.

1 When you are at the airport, make sure you always ....

2 You must always .... when you are in the car.

3 The easiest way to get around in London is to ....

4 Get back! You have to .... or you might get hurt.

5 When you get on the train, ... between the train and the platform.

2 Use the adjectives in the list to complete the sentences.

- fast • cheap • expensive • comfortable
- enjoyable • safe • convenient • slow
- tiring

1 Travelling by plane is *expensive* **but** *fast/fast* **and** *convenient*

2 Travelling by car is ....

3 Travelling by coach is ....

4 Travelling by train is ....

5 Travelling by boat is ....

6 Travelling on a bike is ....

Reading

3 **a.** Read the advertisements A & B and mark the statements 1-6 *R* (right), *W* (wrong) or *DS* (doesn't say).

A

Rome 3-NIGHT CITY BREAK

4-STAR HOTEL

- See the sights, including the world famous Colosseum.
- Do your shopping in Rome's stylish shops & boutiques.
- Dine in our luxury restaurant.
- Work out in the hotel gym.
- Swim in the heated indoor pool.

Hurry! Book by 30th Oct. & save up to 50%!

www.eurobreaks.co.uk

B

Cool Springs

HOLIDAY VILLAGE

✓ Stay in our brand-new self-catering apartments.

✓ Eat in our excellent snack-bars and restaurants.

✓ Take a tennis or sailing lesson.

✓ Go horse-riding.

✓ Relax by the pool.

Children under 5 go free!

Call now for the new Spring/Summer brochure: 0845 1245986

1 The hotel in advertisement A is near a shopping centre. ....

2 There is a pool inside the hotel in advertisement A. ....

3 There is a discount for the trip to Rome. ....

4 You pay half price for a 3-year-old child in the holiday village. ....

5 The place in advertisement B is near the sea. ....

6 You can do different sports in the holiday village. ....

b. Tell your partner which of the two places you would choose for your holiday and why.

Vocabulary Practice

1 Use the verbs in the list to complete the sentences below.

- let • exchanged • sang • wore • put
- danced • made • ate • dressed • watched

1 They .... up the decorations in the morning and then they .... wreaths and pumpkin lanterns.
2 They all .... the parade and at the end they .... off spectacular fireworks.
3 It was Halloween and the children .... up as witches and ghosts.
4 We first .... gifts and then we .... stuffed turkey. After dinner, we gathered around the piano and .... traditional songs.
5 Last year on May Day, we .... our colourful costumes and .... around the Maypole.

Everyday English
(Catching up on news)

2 Use the phrases in the box to complete the dialogue.

- It sounds like you've been really busy
- We have a lot of catching up to do
- Sounds great
- It's been a long time
- Where have you been

A: Hey Martin! **1)** ....?
I haven't seen you in ages!
B: I know. **2)** ....!
A: What's up?
B: Well, I was in Paris for three months. I got back last week.
A: Paris? **3)** ....! Was it business or pleasure?
B: Business. My company sent me there for a training programme.
A: **4)** ....
B: Yes, I have. Listen, we should get together for coffee or something. **5)** ....
....
A: Absolutely! Are you free now?
B: I am, actually. Let's go!

Speaking

3 Look at the pictures and describe them to your partner. Talk about:

- where the people are • actions happening
- reason for celebration • people's clothes
- people's feelings

4 You went to a party last night. Tell your partner:

- where you went
- what the party was for
- what you did
- your feelings

An email describing a festival

1 Imagine you are at the festival shown in the pictures. What can you see/hear/do there? How do you feel?

2 a. Read the email. Which of your ideas from Ex.1 does Emily mention?

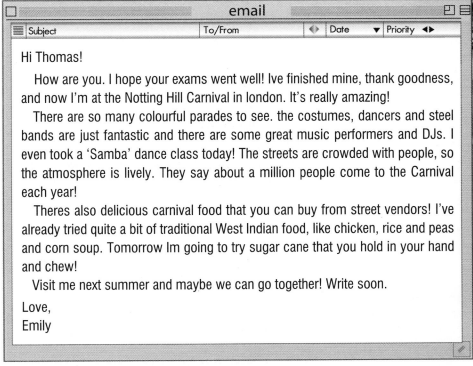

---

email

| Subject | To/From | ◆ | Date | ▼ | Priority | ◆▶ |

Hi Thomas!

How are you. I hope your exams went well! Ive finished mine, thank goodness, and now I'm at the Notting Hill Carnival in london. It's really amazing!

There are so many colourful parades to see. the costumes, dancers and steel bands are just fantastic and there are some great music performers and DJs. I even took a 'Samba' dance class today! The streets are crowded with people, so the atmosphere is lively. They say about a million people come to the Carnival each year!

Theres also delicious carnival food that you can buy from street vendors! I've already tried quite a bit of traditional West Indian food, like chicken, rice and peas and corn soup. Tomorrow Im going to try sugar cane that you hold in your hand and chew!

Visit me next summer and maybe we can go together! Write soon.

Love,
Emily

---

b. Read again. Which of the following does Emily include in her email? Put a tick (✓) or a cross (✗). Where does she write each item? (e.g. 1st paragraph, at the top of the email etc.)

closing remarks ☐ opening remarks ☐
the food ☐ address ☐ date ☐
what she saw and did ☐ greeting ☐

3 a. Find six punctuation mistakes in the email (e.g. capital letters, full stops etc.).

b. Underline all the adjectives in the text. What does each describe?

Your turn

4 Read the rubric and answer the questions.

> Imagine you are at a famous festival or celebration in your country. Write your pen friend an email about the things you can see or do.

1 To whom are you writing?
2 Which festival are you going to choose? What is it like? What can you see/do there? Complete the spidergram.

activities

3 What are you going to write in each paragraph?
4 How will you begin and end your email?

5 Write your email. Use the email in Ex. 2 as a model. Check the punctuation carefully.

Present Perfect

1 Complete the *past participles* of the verbs below. Which are irregular?

1	arrive	12	lose	....
2	be	13	meet	....
3	buy	14	stay	....
4	come	15	put	....
5	eat	16	return	....
6	fly	17	ride	....
7	get	18	see	....
8	go	19	take	....
9	have	20	tell	....
10	keep	21	travel	....
11	leave	22	try	....

2 Use the prompts and the *present perfect* to say what has happened in each picture.

- finish studies • buy house • get married
- get lost • score goal • miss bus

1 *They have got married.*

3 Complete the sentences with the *present perfect* of the verbs in brackets.

1 ....
(you/ever/be) on holiday abroad?

2 It's late! I'm sure we ....
(miss) the boat.

3 This dirty hotel room ....
(ruin) my holiday.

4 Julia and I .... (not/decide)
where to go on holiday this summer.

5 Mark .... (just/tell)
me that he can't go away with me.

6 We .... (meet) some very nice
people here and we're having a great time.

7 The Harrisons .... (buy) a nice
beach house and they ....
(invite) us to spend the summer with them.

8 John ....
(not/come) back from his trip yet.

4 Read the exchanges. In which exchange has someone visited a place and *a) is still there? b) has come back?* Which verb do we use in each case?

1 A: Have you ever visited Asia?
  B: Yes, **I've been to** China and Singapore.

2 A: Where's Tony?
  B: **He's gone to** England. He's coming back on Saturday.

5 Fill in: *have/has been (to)* or *have/has gone (to).*

A: Where is Jane?
B: She **1)** .... Italy. She's back next week.
A: Italy, really?
B: Yes. **2)** .... you ever .... Italy?
A: Yes, I **3)** .... Naples and Rome. They're beautiful cities.
B: Jane **4)** .... Naples, too. This time she **5)** .... Venice and Florence.
A: Oh, I **6)** .... never ....Venice. I've heard it's great.
B: It is. I **7)** .... once and I absolutely loved it!

For – Since

6 Fill in: *for* or *since.*

1 Greg hasn't been on holidays .... ages.
2 I haven't visited London .... 2000.

3 Kate hasn't cleaned the beach house .... last summer.
4 They have been away .... three weeks.
5 They have had the flat .... 1980.

7 Complete the questions with the words from the list. In pairs, ask and answer the questions.

• play • eat • see • read • meet • climb • be • travel

1 A: *Have you ever seen* the Atlantic?
  B: *Yes, I have. /No, I haven't.*
2 A: .... in a Thai restaurant?
  B: ....
3 A: .... a person from Australia?
  B: ....
4 A: .... a tree?
  B: ....
5 A: .... cricket?
  B: ....
6 A: .... in an aeroplane?
  B: ....
7 A: .... a book in a week?
  B: ....
8 A: .... to the theatre?
  B: ....

8 Put the verbs in brackets into the *simple past* or the *present perfect*.

1 A: ....
     (you/ever/celebrate) Halloween?
  B: Of course. Last year we ....
     (make) a huge pumpkin lantern.
2 A: We .... (just/come) back from the parade. It .... (be) fun.
  B: Really? I think that the one last year .... (be) much better. More schools .... (take) part in that one.
3 A: .... (you/go) to the balloon launch this morning?
  B: No. I .... (be) to the Balloon Festival before and I can't say I .... (like) it.
4 A: Where .... (you/be)?
  B: I .... (go) to the opening day of the Tulip Festival.

A: Oh! .... (you/enjoy) it?
B: Very much!
5 A: .... (you/attend) any festivals while you .... (be) in Korea?
  B: Yes, and I even .... (buy) some souvenirs. I .... (bring) you this colourful fan.
6 A: .... (you/enjoy) the film?
  B: Yes, it was very interesting.
7 A: Does John still work at the National Bank?
  B: Yes, he .... (be) there for 10 years.
8 A: When ....
     .... (Christopher Columbus/ **discover**) America?
  B: In 1492.
9 A: .... (you/write) the letter yet?
  B: No, I haven't.
10 A: Who is that man?
   B: He's an artist. He .... (paint) a lot of beautiful pictures.
11 A: What time does the train leave?
   B: It .... (just/leave).
12 A: Is the new restaurant good?
   B: I don't know. I .... (not/eat) there yet.

9 Fill in: *already, just, yet, never, ever, last, ago.* Then, match 1-5 to a-e to make exchanges.

1 ☐ Have you booked the plane tickets ......?
2 ☐ I have .... travelled to Asia. What's it like?
3 ☐ Have you .... been to Kenya?
4 ☐ Why don't we go to Barcelona? We had a great time .... summer.
5 ☐ It's very noisy next door. It seems the Johnsons have .... come back from their trip.

a I've .... been there twice. I'd like to go somewhere different this year.
b I think they came back .... night.
c No, I've .... been there.
d I went to China three years .... It was amazing!
e Actually, I booked them two days ....

25

1 a. Look at the title of the article. What do you think the article is about? Read the introduction and check.

b. Read the article. Which places are mentioned?

FESTIVALS ON FIRE!

This week on our 'Culture Now' page, we take a look at some of the noisiest and most colourful festivals and traditions around the world. All of these festivals have a common theme: fire!

In Britain, a man called Guy Fawkes and twelve other men planned to blow up the English Parliament and King James I on 5th November, 1605. Every year on this day, people organise firework displays and build huge bonfires to burn dummies of Guy Fawkes. Children love to wave sparklers and sometimes people eat special 'Bonfire Night' food, such as warm soup, sausages or even baked potatoes cooked around the base of the fire.

In the Shetland Islands, Scotland, a similar festival called "Up Helly Aa" takes place. Every year, on the last Tuesday in January, local people take part in parades and fire festivals to remember the islands' link to the Vikings. People dress up in Viking costumes, drag a longboat through the streets and finally throw fire torches into it and watch it burn.

Maybe you like to celebrate New Year with a bang? In some cities in Colombia, people put little fireworks inside a doll with objects that bring unhappy memories. At midnight on New Year's Eve, they burn the doll to forget everything bad that happened that year. In some villages in Scotland, people set barrels of tar on fire at New Year and roll them through the streets. They do this to burn up the old year and let the new year in.

2 Read again and complete the table below. Then, explain the highlighted words.

Festival & Country	When?	What happens?
Guy Fawkes, Britain	1)	firework displays, bonfires, sparklers and special food
2)	3)	people dress up in Viking costumes and burn a longboat
4)	midnight on New Year's Eve	people burn a doll with fireworks and objects inside it
New Year, Scotland	New Year	5) ....

3 In pairs, use the table in Ex. 2 to interview each other about one of the festivals in the text.

4 Is there a similar festival in your country? Make notes under the headings, then tell the class.

• name • place • reason • activities

Progress Check

Vocabulary & Grammar

A Circle the correct item.

1 Stuart likes .... diving. He goes to Acapulco every summer.
   A jet   B cliff   C water

2 Kate and I have been friends ....
   1995.
   A for   B in   C since

3 Luke has .... flown in a plane; this will be his first time.
   A never   B ever   C already

4 Where .... on holiday last year?
   A have you gone   B did you go
   C you went

5 I think I'll just .... by the pool this afternoon.
   A swim   B relax   C visit

6 How long .... about this?
   A did you know   B you have known
   C have you known

7 This hotel looks very .... How much does a double room cost?
   A luxurious   B delicious
   C colourful

8 Have you ever .... a camel? It's quite an experience!
   A ride   B rode   C ridden

9 Fiona has been a tour guide .... ten years.
   A since   B from   C for

10 We are going to .... on a cruise ship; I'm so excited!
   A ride   B fly   C travel

11 There's a beautiful .... beach right in front of the hotel.
   A sandy   B cobbled   C bright

12 .... your seatbelts, please.
   A Mind   B Stand   C Fasten

13 Do you like .... food? You should try Indian then.
   A cobbled   B spicy   C luxurious

14 We .... Spain twice so far.
   A have visited   B visited   C visit

15 Did you .... decorations for your party?
   A exchange   B wear   C put up

16 Why don't you .... this local dish?
   A try   B take   C buy

17 You can .... the Underground in London; it's very convenient.
   A hire   B use   C keep

18 Paula has .... come back from her trip. Her suitcase is still unpacked.
   A just   B yet   C already

19 Last night they let off .... in the centre of the town.
   A fireworks   B gifts   C parades

20 He .... never done bungee jumping before.
   A has   B hasn't   C not has

$$\left(\begin{array}{c} \text{Marks:} \ \overline{} \\ \text{20x3} \quad 60 \end{array}\right)$$

Everyday English

B Match the sentences (1-5) to the responses (a-e).

1	How may I help you?
2	Where have you been?
3	How much does it cost?
4	Have you ever tried paella?
5	I haven't seen you for ages!

a Prices start at £300.
b I've been really busy these past few weeks.
c I'd like to book two plane tickets, please.
d No. What's it like?
e I was in Vienna on business.

$$\left(\begin{array}{c} \text{Marks:} \ \overline{} \\ \text{5x8} \quad 40 \end{array}\right)$$

$$\left(\begin{array}{c} \text{Total:} \ \overline{} \\ \text{100 marks} \end{array}\right)$$

27

4a — Come rain or shine!

Vocabulary Practice

1 **a.** Match the pictures to the correct weather description.

  a cool & cloudy with heavy rain
  b warm & sunny
  c rainy & windy
  d freezing cold & snowy
  e chilly & foggy   f sunny spells & showers

b. What's the weather like today where you are? How does it make you feel?

2 Circle the odd word out.

1 boiling, chilly, mild, autumn
2 ice, cloud, snow, west
3 depressed, relaxed, foggy, stressed
4 sunshine, spring, summer, winter
5 storm, rain, wind, fog
6 east, north, season, south

Everyday English
(Permission)

3 Choose *a* or *b* to complete the exchanges.

1 A: Can we go to the beach today?
    B: **a** No, it's not.
       b Of course!

2 A: Could we go on a bike ride, Dad?
    B: **a** Look at those clouds!
       b Sure! It's not raining now.

3 A: Mum, I'm bored! Can I watch a video?
    B: **a** I'm afraid you can't.
       b Are you sure?

Listening

4 You will hear five short conversations. For questions 1-5 tick (✓) the correct answer (*A*, *B* or *C*).

1 What is the weather like in Paris?

  A ☐   B ☐   C ☐

2 Where does Paul want to go for his holidays?

Scotland   **Italy**   **Spain**

  A ☐   B ☐   C ☐

3 What is the temperature now?

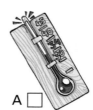 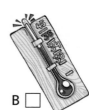 

  A ☐   B ☐   C ☐

4 What will John need to take with him this weekend?

  A ☐   B ☐   C ☐

5 What will they do?

  A ☐   B ☐   C ☐

Vocabulary Practice

1 a. Match the pictures (A-H) to the descriptions (1-8), then label them.

A [1] d _ _ _ _ _

B [ ] r _ _ _ _

C [ ] w _ _ _ _ _ _ _ _

D [ ] (i _ _ _ _ _ _)

E [ ] l _ _ _

F [ ] b _ _ _ _

G [ ] o _ _ _ _

H [ ] f _ _ _ _ _

1 An area of land where there is almost no water, rain, trees or plants.
2 A large area where trees grow close together.
3 An area of sand or stones beside the sea.
4 A large area of fresh water with land surrounding it.
5 A piece of land with water all around it.
6 A place where water flows over a steep, high cliff in hills or mountains.
7 A very large area of sea.
8 A large amount of fresh water that flows in a long line across the land.

Reading

2 You are going to read a text about Antarctica. Which of the following words do you expect to find? Read and check.

- temperature • driest
- ice • rain • forest
- fresh water • animal
- snow • desert • beach
- freezing • sunny spells

3 a. Read again and fill in the gaps (1-8) with the correct word.

   b. What do the following numbers refer to?

- 70% • 98%
- 1983 • -89°C
- 5 • 90% • 2 million

@ Internet Explorer

www.homeworkhelp.com

•••••••••••• **GEOGRAPHY**

Grab your winter coat, gloves and hat because we're going to take a look 0) at the coldest place on Earth! Scientists recorded a temperature of −89°C there 1) .... 1983 – the lowest temperature ever recorded on Earth! Antarctica isn't just the coldest place on Earth, but 2) ..... wettest and driest place, too. 'But that's impossible!' you say. Well, no actually! Ice covers 98% of Antarctica. In fact, it has 90% of all the ice and 70% of 3) ..... the fresh water in the whole world! So how can Antarctica also be the driest place on Earth? Well, about the same amount of precipitation (rain 4) ..... snow) falls there as in the Sahara desert. Basically, that's not a lot - less 5) ..... 5 cm per year. In one interior region of Antarctica, called The Dry Valleys, the last time 6) ..... rained was about 2 million years ago! This is because 7) ..... very strong winds that drive away all the moisture in the air. With freezing temperatures, no water, and no animal or plant life, conditions in The Dry Valleys are 8) ..... bit like conditions on the planet Mars!

Click here to find out more about this chilly destination!

Vocabulary Practice

1 Name the animals in the pictures, then complete the crossword. Use plurals. Which animal has got: *hooves, paws, antlers, feathers, shell, wings, a beak?*

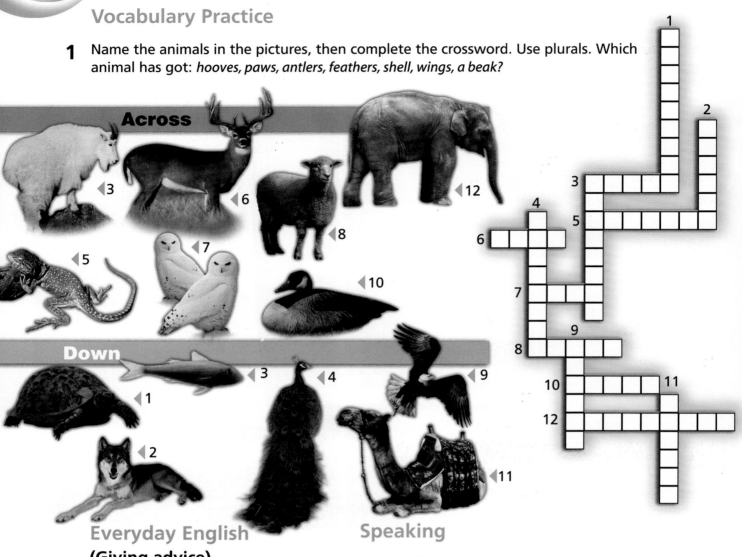

Across

Down

Everyday English
(Giving advice)

2 Complete the exchanges with a phrase from the list.

- Great idea • I don't think so
- I'm not sure

1 A: Have you thought of getting a dog, Grandma?
   B: ....
   They are a lot of work!

2 A: Why don't you get a pet?
   B: ....
   it's such a good idea. I work really long hours.

3 A: How about getting a rabbit for Sarah?
   B: ....!
   She really loves animals.

Speaking

3 a. Describe the animals in the pictures.

   b. Use the people's profiles to discuss what kind of pet is best for each person. Give reasons.

a Kathy – lives in a flat, doesn't have a garden, works long hours
b Tom – 80 years old, lives alone, doesn't go out much
c Simon – 7 years old, lives in a big house with a garden
d Hayley – loves animals, works part-time, already has a dog

A: *Kathy lives in a small flat without a garden, so I don't think a dog is the best pet for her.*
B: *Yes, I agree. Also, she works long hours and dogs need to go for walks. What about a goldfish? etc.*

30

An article – describing a place

1 Look at the pictures. Where could they be? What is it like? How do you think the people live? What kind of animals live there? Read and check.

Like No Other Place On Earth!

▶ Alaska is the USA's 49ᵗʰ state and is **situated** to the north west of Canada. It covers 586,000 square miles 1) .... is America's largest **state**. In fact, it is one fifth the size of the whole of the USA!

▶ Alaska is a beautiful state full of rich countryside and wildlife. It has 100,000 **glaciers**, 3,000 rivers 2) .... 3 million lakes! It also has the highest mountain in North America, Mount McKinley. Thousands of bears, eagles, wolves, moose (a kind of deer), sea lions and whales live in its oceans, green forests 3) .... snow-covered mountains.

▶ The **population** of Alaska is almost 650,000. Around 40% of the state's **residents** live in the largest city, Anchorage, in the south. This is because most of the state is very difficult to **reach** by car. It can be very cold and dark in the winter, 4) .... conditions are ideal for exciting activities such as skiing, snowboarding, ice fishing 5) .... dog sledding.

▶ Alaska is an amazing, **record-breaking** place. It is like no other place on Earth!

2 Read again and fill in the gaps (1-5) with: **and**, **or** or **but**. Then, explain the words in bold.

3 Match the paragraphs (1-4) to the descriptions (a-d).

- a ☐ geographical features and wildlife
- b ☐ introduction (name, location, some general information)
- c ☐ conclusion (summarises the text)
- d ☐ people

4 Underline the topic sentences in the main body paragraphs. In pairs, suggest other appropriate ones.

Your turn

5 **a.** Read the rubric and underline the key words. What are you going to write about? Who is going to read it?

> *A children's geography magazine has asked its readers to send in articles about interesting geographical locations. Write your article, describing a location, and include information about its geographical features, wildlife and people.*

b. Look at the notes below. What are you going to include in each paragraph?

The Sahara Desert

Location: Covers most of North Africa, same size as USA
Size: largest desert in world/9 million sq. km
Geographical features: rocks, some underground rivers, sand dunes, flat areas of sand, high mountains
Weather: very little rainfall, temperatures 13˚C - 50˚C
Animal/plant life: 1,200 species of plants that can live in hot, dry conditions e.g. grasses, cacti. Rich wildlife e.g. foxes, hedgehogs, ostriches, owls, frogs, crocodiles, lizards, cobras
Population: 2.5 million
Life in the Sahara: difficult living conditions; people live around 'oases' (where water breaks through the surface); camel caravans transport food across desert

c. Think of appropriate topic sentences for the main body paragraphs.

6 Write your article (100-120 words). Give it an interesting title.

The definite article (the)

1 Fill in *the* where necessary.

1) ...... China, 2) (...... People's Republic of China), is situated in eastern 3) ...... Asia, bordering 4) ...... Pacific in the east. It is 5) ...... third largest country in the world, next to 6) ...... Canada and 7) ...... Russia, and it has an area of 9.6 million square km. It begins from the point where 8) ...... Heilong and Wusuli rivers meet in the east to 9) ...... Pamirs, the mountain range in the west; and from the midstream of the Heilong River in 10) ...... north to 11) ...... Zengmu'ansha island in 12) ...... South China Sea. 13) ...... Yangtze River, which is 6,300 km long is 14) ...... China's longest river and third in the world after 15) ...... Amazon and 16) ...... Nile. There are 6,536 islands in 17) ...... China. 18) ...... largest is 19) ...... Taiwan, with a total area of about 36,000 square km. 20) ...... South China Sea Islands are the southernmost island group of China.

Comparatives/Superlatives

2 Use the adjectives to write comparisons, as in the examples.

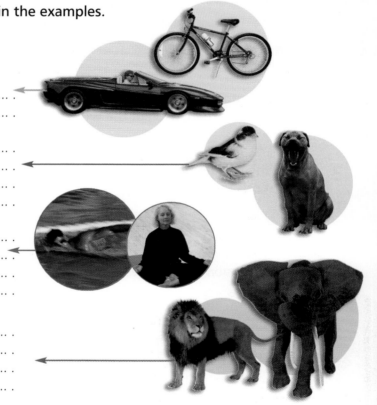

1   **expensive, slow, heavy, cheap**
    A car is *more expensive than a bicycle.*
    A bicycle *is slower than a car.*
    A car is ....
    A bicycle is ....

2   **friendly, small, intelligent, light**
    A dog is ....
    A bird is ....
    A dog is ....
    A bird is ....

3   **difficult, easy, interesting, good**
    Yoga is ....
    Swimming is ....
    Yoga is ....
    Swimming is ....

4   **dangerous, fat, beautiful, big**
    A lion is ....
    An elephant is ....
    A lion is ....
    An elephant is ....

3 Use the information in the table and the *comparative* or *superlative* form of the adjectives in brackets to complete the sentences.

OCEANS	size (in million square metres)	depth (lowest point) (in metres)	length of coastline (in kilometres)
the Pacific	155,557	10,924	135,663
the Atlantic	76,762	8,605	111,866
the Indian	68,556	7,258	66,526
the Southern	20,327	7,235	17,968
the Arctic	14,056	4,665	45,389

1 *The Southern Ocean* is 20,327 million square metres. It is .... the .... Ocean, which is 68,556 million square metres. The .... Ocean is .... of all. **(small)**

2 The .... Ocean's coastline is 111,866 kilometres long. It is .... the .... Ocean's coastline. The .... Ocean's coastline is .... of all. **(short)**

3 The .... Ocean is 7,235 metres deep. It is .... the .... Ocean. The .... Ocean is .... of all. **(deep)**

4 The .... Ocean is 76,762 million square metres. It is .... the .... Ocean, which is 14,056 million square metres. The .... Ocean is .... of all. **(big)**

4 Write sentences to compare the animals below. Use adjectives from the list and *much+comparative* or *as+adjective+as*.

- tall
- big
- small
- dangerous

The giraffe is much taller than the camel.

5 Correct the mistakes.

1 Asia is the most biggest continent of all.
2 The weather in Brazil is best than the weather in Britain.
3 The Nile is the longer than the Amazon.
4 Mount Everest is much higher as Mont Blanc.
5 Lake Baikal is the deeper lake in the world.
6 The Sonoran desert is larger of the Thar desert.
7 Australia is more smaller than Asia.
8 The weather in Spain is as warm than the weather in Greece.

Question Words

6 a. Fill in the gaps with the correct question word. Then, match questions 1-8 to answers a-h.

- What • Where • Which • How much
- How many • How far • How long
- How fast

Quiz

Bald Eagle

1 .... does the bald eagle live? ......
2 .... feathers does it have? ......
3 .... does it eat? ......
4 .... is bigger, the male or the female bald eagle? ......
5 .... does the bald eagle's nest weigh? ......
6 .... does it have to keep the eggs warm for? ......
7 .... can it fly at top speed? ......
8 .... can it fly in a single day? ......

a 1,770 km.
b The female.
c One to one and a half months.
d 50 km/h.
e Mostly fish.
f Near rivers and large lakes.
g 1 ton.
h 7,000.

b. Use the information in the quiz to talk about the bald eagle.

DUCK-BILLED PLATYPUS

Description

The platypus has a flat body. It has a bill or beak like a duck's, webbed feet with five claws for digging and a short, flat tail. The bill and feet of a platypus are black while the fur is usually a dark brown colour. The platypus swims well but not very fast. While swimming, it has its eyes and ears **shut**. It finds its way with its bill, which also helps it to find food. While **underwater** it stores any food it finds in its **cheeks**. The platypus is a poisonous mammal. Its **poison** can cause pain to man but it can kill smaller animals. Its fur is one of the most **waterproof** in the animal kingdom. It is now a protected **species**.

Habitat	Reproduction	Characteristics	Diet	Senses
You can find the platypus in Eastern Australia, in and around streams and rivers. It lives in holes underground.	The platypus is one of only two mammals which lay eggs (the other is the echidna, an anteater also from Australia).	The platypus is a shy animal that spends most of its time alone. It sleeps during the day and comes out at night.	The platypus eats shrimps, frogs and fish eggs.	With its bill, the platypus can sense the creatures it wants to eat. It also has an excellent sense of sight and hearing.

1 Look at the picture. Choose words from the list to describe the platypus.

- brown fur
- hooves
- feathers
- paws
- short, flat tail
- bill
- long whiskers
- webbed feet
- short legs
- fat body

The platypus is a mammal. It has got ... .

2 Look at the headings in the text. What do you expect to read in each section? Read and check.

3 Read again and circle the correct answer.

1 The platypus finds its food in the water.
   A Right   B Wrong   C Doesn't say
2 Its poison can kill a person.
   A Right   B Wrong   C Doesn't say
3 Many mammals lay eggs.
   A Right   B Wrong   C Doesn't say
4 The platypus sleeps 20 hours a day.
   A Right   B Wrong   C Doesn't say
5 The platypus can see and hear well.
   A Right   B Wrong   C Doesn't say

4 Read the text again and explain the words in bold.

5 Talk about an unusual animal which lives in your country. Give information about:

- its name • where it lives • what it looks like
- what it eats

Progress Check

Vocabulary & Grammar

A Circle the correct item.

1 I like cold weather, that's why I love
   ....
   A summer   B winter   C autumn

2 Tomorrow will be a ...., sunny day.
   A foggy   B hot   C wet

3 When I travelled to Africa, I had the
   .... time of my life.
   A better   B good   C best

4 On that day in Cairo we almost died! The
   temperature reached 37°C, it was
   ....
   A bitterly cold   B boiling hot
   C freezing cold

5 She's .... cat I've ever seen.
   A the beautiful   B more beautiful
   C the most beautiful

6 It was so ....; I couldn't even see the
   car in front of me.
   A foggy   B cloudy   C wet

7 Cats have got ....
   A feathers   B whiskers   C beaks

8 I will take a jacket with me in case it gets
   a bit ....
   A warm   B mild   C chilly

9 France is .... expensive than China.
   A more   B most   C much

10 .... legs do spiders have?
    A How much   B How long
    C How many

11 Maria and John like water sports so they
    usually spend their holidays on ....
    A forests   B islands   C valleys

12 We need .... than ten days to
    explore the Amazon forests.
    A much   B most   C more

13 Barcelona is a nice and .... city.
    A boring   B friendly
    C stressful

14 Dolphins are much .... than goldfish.
    A smarter   B smart   C smartest

15 Ann's parrot is as noisy .... mine.
    A than   B as   C that

16 .... do camels live?
    A Which   B Who   C Where

17 This hamster is more playful .... the
    previous one we had.
    A from   B than   C as

18 I'm writing this letter to ask .... her
    advice.
    A for   B about   C with

19 Tomorrow will be chilly but with some
    .... spells.
    A windy   B sunny   C stormy

20 That was the .... holiday we've ever
    had!
    A worse   B bad   C worst

$$\left(\begin{array}{c} \text{Marks: } \overline{} \\ \text{20x3} \quad 60 \end{array}\right)$$

Everyday English

B Complete the sentences.

- You should
- Have you thought
- Why don't you
- I'm afraid you can't
- Great idea

1 A: .... come with us?
   B: I'm not sure I can.

2 A: Could I borrow your umbrella?
   B: .... I need it.

3 A: .... of buying a pet?
   B: I don't think it's a good idea.

4 A: How about going to the beach?
   B: ....!

5 A: .... buy a fish.
   B: I think you are right.

$$\left(\begin{array}{c} \text{Marks: } \overline{} \\ \text{5x8} \quad 40 \end{array}\right)$$

$$\left(\begin{array}{c} \text{Total: } \overline{} \\ \text{100 marks} \end{array}\right)$$

Vocabulary Practice

1 Underline the disasters in the headlines. Then, fill in the correct word.

- blows • destroyed • collapse • rescues • lava

Town 1) .... in worst flood in 100 years

Young boy 2) .... sister from fire

Hurricane 3) .... roofs off

Buildings 4) .... in huge earthquake

5) .... flows through valley in volcanic eruption

2 Complete the spidergrams with as many words as you can think of.

Volcanic eruption

Earthquake

Flood

3 Circle the correct word.

1 The earthquake was terrifying. Buildings were **shaking/blowing** and people were running everywhere.
2 They didn't know what to do. The flames were **wobbling/spreading** fast.
3 The wind was very strong. Objects were **smashing/swaying** into buildings.
4 The flood was **terrifying/howling**. Water was flowing into houses and cars were floating down the street.

Speaking

4 Imagine you lived through one of the scenes in the pictures. Use the notes and any of your own ideas to describe to your partner what happened and what it was like.

hurricane/wind howling/trees swaying/destroy houses, cars, property/people afraid, screaming, running, some injured

flood/heavy rain/storms/dirty water flowing down street/many homes flooded, damaged/people shocked, worried, upset

36

Vocabulary Practice

1 Find ten parts of the body in the wordsearch.

H	E	A	D	Z	W	H	T	U	H
F	O	O	T	Z	W	A	O	O	H
Q	Z	O	Y	U	E	N	E	E	T
P	I	G	R	L	V	D	V	S	U
V	J	P	W	K	N	E	E	F	F
L	E	P	U	G	Q	B	X	Z	I
E	A	N	K	L	E	A	Y	S	N
G	W	R	B	I	O	C	E	L	G
O	P	A	R	M	F	K	V	G	E
U	T	O	X	N	W	W	G	W	R

2 Fill in the correct word.

- grazed • broke • cut
- ankle • tooth • hurts

1 Mark .... his knee and twisted his .... in the football game yesterday.
2 I burnt my hand while I was taking the cake out of the oven. It really ....!
3 Oh no! I think I've broken a ....!
4 Mike stepped on a piece of glass and .... his toe.
5 My grandma's in hospital. She slipped in some water and .... her leg.

Reading

3 **a.** Read the title and look at the picture. What do you think the story might be about? Read and check.

Wonderdog Pulls Owner from Car Crash

Endal the wonderdog, already named *Dog of the Millennium* and *Brightest Dog on Earth*, made national news headlines again yesterday after a car hit his owner's wheelchair outside a hotel.

In 1991, Allen Parton was sitting outside the hotel when the speeding car threw him from his chair and knocked him out. While he was unconscious, Endal rolled him over with his teeth into the recovery position. After this, he got a blanket from his bag and covered him with it! The dog then got Allen's mobile phone out of his bag and held the phone up to his face. Finally, he ran back to the hotel and barked until people came out to help. Allen didn't know that Endal could do any of these things!

Mr Parton was disabled from the tragic accident. For years now, Endal has been everything to him; his best friend, his banker, his travel agent, his home help and many other things. 'He even buys the ticket on the bus and collects it from the machine,' says Allen. 'He has helped me in so many ways.'

b. Read the article and choose the correct answer (*A, B* or *C*).

1 Endal made the headlines again when
   A a hotel worker hit his owner.
   B his owner was in an accident.
   C he became *Brightest Dog on Earth*.

2 When the accident happened, Allen
   A was just arriving at a hotel.
   B was sitting outside a hotel.
   C was at a dog show.

3 The first thing Endal did after the accident was
   A roll Allen over and cover him with a blanket.
   B run back to the hotel and get help.
   C get Allen's mobile phone from his bag.

4 Endal is important to Allen because
   A he buys his ticket on the bus.
   B he's a very friendly dog.
   C he helps him with many things.

c. Where could you read a text like this one? Suggest another title for it.

37

Vocabulary Practice

1 **Match the words. Then, use them to complete the sentences.**

1	road	a	disaster
2	plane	b	crash
3	environmental	c	members
4	crew	d	service
5	mountain	e	guard
6	fire	f	accident
7	coast	g	rescue

1 The traffic was terrible this morning. I think it was because of a bad ....

2 There were lots of boats in trouble during the storm last night. The .... had to rescue them.

3 The ship that sank off the coast of Canada last week caused a huge oil slick. It's a terrible ....

4 "Jo, did you hear? There's been an awful .... over the Atlantic Ocean. They say over 100 people have been killed."

5 The climbers got into trouble when it started to snow heavily. Fortunately, a .... team found them in time.

6 The .... fought for hours to put out the flames, but unfortunately most of the forest was destroyed.

7 The heroic pilot saved the lives of 120 passengers and six ....

2 **Circle the odd one out.**

1 poisoning, drowning, disaster, explosion
2 ambulance, coast guard, police, fire
3 collide, land, crash, hit
4 plane, pilot, crew, passengers
5 electrocute, ankle, poison, cut

Everyday English

(Giving news & reacting)

3 **Use the phrases to complete the dialogues.**

- Oh no
- How sad
- You won't believe what happened
- Did you hear

A: **1)** ....?
B: No, what happened?
A: There has been a terrible rail accident and 15 people have died.
B: **2)** ....! That's terrible!

A: **3)** ....!
B: What?
A: A little boy drowned in the lake yesterday.
B: Oh dear! **4)** ....!

Listening

4 You will hear a woman talking about the sinking of a ship. Listen and complete the notes.

The Herald of Free Enterprise

Type of Ship: **0** _ferry_

Route: from **1** to Zeebrugge

Date of disaster: **2** , 1987

Cause of disaster: Crew forgot to close the cargo **3**

Depth of water: **4** feet

Number of people killed: **5**

A story

1 a. Read the rubric and underline the key words. What are you going to write? Why are you writing?

> *Your school is holding a competition to write a story entitled 'A Lucky Escape'. Write a story for the competition.*

b. What kind of things can you have a lucky escape from? Have you ever had a lucky escape? What happened?

2 a. Look at the highlighted words/phrases from the story. What do you think happens in the story? Read and check.

A Lucky escape

It was a bright, sunny day and the start of the summer holidays. 'Let's all go out for a walk in the hills!' my dad said. So, we quickly packed a picnic, jumped into the car and set out for the countryside.

When we got there, we parked the car and had a lovely long walk. Then, while we were enjoying our picnic, we noticed big, black clouds above us. Suddenly, there was a loud clap of thunder and huge raindrops began to fall. We cleared away our picnic and ran under some nearby trees.

Soon, the storm was directly overhead. 'It's not safe under these trees,' Mum said. 'Let's go back to the car.' A few seconds after we all started running, there was an enormous cracking noise behind us. Then, I felt a strange tingling feeling all over my body. I looked back at the trees. They were black and two of them were lying on the ground!

We all got into the car shaking with fear. 'I don't believe it!' Dad gasped. 'Those trees were struck by lightning just after we left them.' My arm still felt strange and my brother's hair was standing on end. We all looked at each other in horror. What a lucky escape!

b. Put the events in the order they happened. Tell the story.

- [ ] The trees were struck by lightning.
- [ ] They sheltered under some trees.
- [ ] They got back into the car.
- [ ] The family had a walk and a picnic.
- [ ] They ran away from the trees.
- [ ] The family decided to go on a trip to the countryside.
- [ ] A storm began.

3 a. Which paragraph(s) in the story: set(s) the scene? develop(s) the story? describe(s) what happens in the end?

b. What tenses are used in the story? What words link ideas/events?

Your turn

4 a. Look at the picture and describe the beginning of the story using the words below. What might happen next? Talk in pairs.

- two friends in a car
- raining heavily
- muddy hill
- slip down hill towards lake

b. Answer the questions.

1 Who are the main characters in the story? How do they feel?
2 What are the main events in order?
3 What is the climax event?
4 What happens in the end?
5 Why is it a 'lucky escape'?

5 Use your answers to Ex. 4b to write your story for the competition (100-120 words).

Past Simple vs Past Continuous

1 Put the verbs in brackets into the *past simple* or the *past continuous*. Which was the longer action in each sentence?

1 My family and I .... (sleep) when our house .... (start) shaking.

2 While the ground .... (shake), several things .... (fall) off our kitchen cabinets and bookshelves.

3 My bed .... (move) from side to side when the earthquake suddenly .... (stop).

4 Just as we .... (try) to recover from the shock, there .... (be) an aftershock.

5 As we .... (run) for the door, a lamp .... (crash) to the floor.

2 Put the verbs in brackets into the *past simple* or the *past continuous*.

It was evening and I **1)** .... (watch) television with my parents. The TV news **2)** .... (give) constant flood warnings as Hurricane Floyd **3)** .... (approach). We were worried but we **4)** .... (decide) to stay in our house. Later that night, at 3 am, a policeman **5)** .... (knock) on our door and told us that the water levels **6)** .... (rise). He also **7)** .... (tell) us that we should move our valuables to safety. I barely **8)** .... (sleep) that night I was so frightened.

In the morning I **9)** .... (look) out of the window. It was a beautiful day and the sun **10)** .... (shine). People **11)** .... (walk) by my house up to their knees in water. I **12)** .... (go) downstairs to the kitchen and it was flooded and damaged. We **13)** .... (pack) a few things and **14)** .... (leave).

As we **15)** .... (drive) to a shelter, I **16)** .... (look) back at our house and **17)** .... (cry). All of my things were there.

Past Continuous/When - While

3 Join the sentences using *while* and *when* as in the example.

1 Carol was doing the washing-up. She broke a glass.
   Carol was doing the washing-up when she broke a glass.
   While Carol was doing the washing-up, she broke a glass.

2 Daniel was having dinner. Emma came in.
   ....
   ....

3 Tim was playing the violin. The doorbell rang.
   ....
   ....

4 Liz was driving her car. She ran out of fuel.
   ....
   ....

5 Ross was working in the garden. It started to rain.
   ....
   ....

6 Stewart was walking in the park. A dog attacked him.
   ....
   ....

4 Use the prompts and *when* or *while* to make sentences, as in the example.

He was playing football when he grazed his knee.

play football/graze knee

cut finger/slice bread

eat sweets/break tooth

ride bike/hurt back

ski/break arm

burn hand/make omelette

jog/twist ankle

Reflexive pronouns

5 Fill in the blanks with the correct reflexive pronoun.

1 Do you like this bookcase? My dad made it ....

2 She is too old to look after .... and needs a housekeeper.

3 I don't want to go to the doctor by ....

4 Greg didn't take the car to the garage. He repaired it ....

5 "Who painted your kitchen?" "Nobody, we painted it ...."

6 They don't live with their parents. They live by ....

Mustn't - Can

6 Fill in *mustn't* or *can*.

1 Don't go close to the fireplace; you .... burn yourself.

2 You .... run down the stairs; it's dangerous.

3 People .... light matches in the forest; they .... start a fire.

4 Clean the broken glass from the floor; someone .... cut themselves.

5 Don't give the scissors to the baby; she .... hurt herself.

6 You .... ride your bike in the middle of the road; it's not safe.

Past Perfect

7 Use the headlines below to complete the sentences.

> **Train crashes on outskirts of London**

> **Boy goes missing after 6th birthday party**

> **Driver loses control of vehicle causing serious accident**

> **Plane crashes two minutes after take off**

> **Ship sinks just outside harbour**

1 The boy *had* just *had* (have) his 6th birthday party when he *went* (go) missing.

2 The train .... just .... (reach) London when it .... (crash).

3 The accident .... (happen) because the driver .... (lose) control of his car.

4 The ship .... just .... (leave) the harbour when it .... (sink).

5 The plane .... only .... (take off) two minutes before it .... (crash).

8 Underline the correct tense.

1 Helen **got/had got** into the car when she **realised/was realising** she **forgot/had forgotten** her bag at home.

2 Susan **watched/was watching** TV while Rita **had read/was reading** her book.

3 When I **had got/got** to the scene of the car accident, the police **had already arrived/arrived**.

4 While Fred **was driving/drove** past the factory, there **was/had been** a huge blast.

5 The skiers **were spending/had spent** five days in the mountains before the mountain rescue team **found/had found** them.

6 We **were walking/walked** in the forest when it suddenly **was starting/started** pouring rain.

7 We **called/were calling** 999 and **told/had told** the operator that we **needed/had needed** an ambulance.

8 A man **was hijacking/hijacked** the plane while we **were flying/flew** to London.

5 Reader's Corner

1 How much do you know about cyclones? Guess if the statements 1 to 5 are *T* (true) or *F* (false). Then, read and check.

1 Scientists are not sure exactly how cyclones happen. ....
2 Cyclones are always formed over cool ocean water. ....
3 Cyclones always twist anti-clockwise. ....
4 Cyclone winds can travel as fast as 250km per hour. ....
5 Scientists are not always able to warn people about cyclones. ....

2 Look at the highlighted words. How do they differ? Think of more examples.

3 a. Give each paragraph a heading.

 b. Make notes under each heading. Use them to talk about cyclones.

CYCLONES

Cyclones are huge storms. They happen over the Atlantic and Pacific Oceans. They can cause great damage when they hit land.

Cyclones form over warm ocean water. They only happen if there are moderate[1] to strong winds blowing in the same direction at sea level. There also has to be a big difference between the atmospheric pressure at sea level and at higher levels.

When a storm becomes a cyclone, winds and clouds start twisting[2] around an "eye". This is the centre of the storm. Everything is calm there. Cyclones twist anti-clockwise[3] if they are in the northern hemisphere, and clockwise if they are in the southern hemisphere. Winds can blow as fast as 250km per hour. When a cyclone hits land, it can damage buildings, trees and cars.

A cyclone can be very dangerous. Thanks to satellites, scientists can spot them early and warn[4] people who live near the coast about them.

[1] not extreme
[2] going round and round
[3] in the opposite direction to the rotating hands of a clock
[4] inform

Progress Check

Vocabulary & Grammar

A **Circle the correct answer.**

1 I was sleeping when I .... a strange noise.
   A heard B hear C was hearing

2 Is 999 the telephone number for the emergency ....?
   A rescue B services C coastguard

3 The building.......... in less than twenty seconds.
   A collapsed B smashed C erupted

4 Maria was .... when she heard about David's car accident.
   A embarrassed B shocked C relieved

5 John and Susan were cleaning the house .... the fire started.
   A when B while C which

6 He .... a tooth and now he's got a terrible toothache.
   A broke B twisted C cut

7 The .... spread and burnt the house down in only a few minutes.
   A flames B flood C wind

8 It was .... heavily when the two cars crashed.
   A raining B rained C rains

9 The fire was burning for an hour before the firefighters ....
   A were coming B came C come

10 My back .... because I was sitting on a chair for nine hours yesterday.
   A hurts B breaks C grazes

11 Maria was playing tennis when she .... her leg.
   A broke B break C was breaking

12 When I felt the ground shaking I realised it was a(n) .... and I ran out of the house.
   A earthquake B hurricane C flood

13 The accident happened .... I was using the cooker.
   A before B after C while

14 You .... touch a socket with wet hands. It's dangerous.
   A can B mustn't C must

15 Don't use the scissors. You might cut ....
   A yourself B herself C itself

16 I'm really scared to use the train after that horrible .... accident on Monday.
   A rail B road C plane

17 He .... the exam five times before he passed it.
   A had failed B was failing C fails

18 You don't have to use the Underground. You .... also walk there.
   A mustn't B can't C can

19 The pilot had to ....the plane in a field due to a technical problem.
   A land B park C put

20 All the .... of the crew wish you a pleasant flight.
   A members B controllers C passengers

$$\left(\begin{array}{c}\text{Marks:} \; \dfrac{}{60} \\ \text{20x3}\end{array}\right)$$

Everyday English

B **Put the sentences of the dialogue in the correct order.**

- [ ] Only five.
- [ ] No, what?
- [ ] That's terrible! Are there any survivors?
- [ ] There was a plane crash.
- [ ] Did you hear what happened?

$$\left(\begin{array}{c}\text{Marks:} \; \dfrac{}{40} \\ \text{5x8}\end{array}\right)$$

$$\left(\begin{array}{c}\text{Total:} \; \dfrac{}{100 \text{ marks}}\end{array}\right)$$

Vocabulary Practice

1 a. What's wrong with each person? Label the pictures, then write sentences.

Janet

t _ _ _ _ _ _ _ _

John

s _ _ _ _ _ _ a _ _ _

Tom

a h _ _ _ _ _ _ _

Susan

a t _ _ _ _ _ _ _ _ _ _

Alex

a s _ _ _ t _ _ _ _ _

Maria

a c _ _ _ _ _

Tom's got a headache.

Peter

e _ _ _ _ _ _

2 Use the phrases to complete the sentences.

- takes painkillers • see a dentist
- have a cough sweet
- stay in bed • call a doctor

1 I'm worried about Sean. He's got a terrible stomach ache. Let's ....

2 You sound terrible, Joe! Here, ...

3 Why don't you .... about that toothache, Sally? You've had it for two days now!

4 Ann usually .... if she has a headache.

5 .... today if you have a temperature! It will go up if you go to work.

Everyday English
(Talking about health problems)

3 Use the phrases to complete the dialogue.

- I think I will • What's the matter
- I've got a really sore throat • Oh dear

A: **1)** ....? You don't look very well.

B: No, I'm not. **2)** ....

A: **3)** ....! Why don't you go to the doctor's?

B: That's a good idea. **4)** I... .

Speaking

4 A friend of yours is complaining of a sore throat. In pairs, act out a conversation.

- Ask what the problem is.
- Suggest a medicine he/she should buy.
- Tell him/her how to get to the nearest chemist's.

Vocabulary Practice

1 Label the pictures. Then, use the prompts (a-f) to make sentences, as in the example.

a sell medicine
b check people's teeth
c operate on people
d make and sell glasses
e take care of people's eyes
f examine people when they don't feel well

An ophthalmologist is a person who takes care of people's eyes.

1 o _ _ _ _ _ _ _ _ _ _ _ _ _ _ 2 c _ _ _ _ _ _ 3 o _ _ _ _ _ _ _

 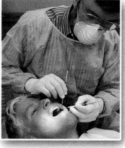 

4 d _ _ _ _ _ 5 d _ _ _ _ _ _ 6 s _ _ _ _ _ _

2 Underline the correct word.

1 Fiona has got a bad **tooth/cough**; she needs to go to the dentist.
2 Why don't you put some ointment on those insect **eyes/ bites**?
3 Try this **cough/pneumonia** syrup; it will make you feel a lot better.
4 Your back is very red; let me rub some **sunburn/aftersun** cream on you.
5 My eyes are very sore; I think it's an eye **infection/operation**.
6 You should take these vitamin C **tablets/glasses** for your cold.

Everyday English
(At the chemist's)

3 Circle the correct item, *a* or *b*.

1 A: a How can I help you?
    b What do you suggest I take for this cough?
B: Try this syrup; it's excellent.

2 A: Can I have something for my cold?
B: a I suggest you take these vitamin C tablets.
    b You won't feel a thing.

3 A: How often should I take them?
B: a Three times a day.
    b On Monday.

4 A: Could I have something for insect bites, please?
B: a I'm afraid these are insect bites.
    b This ointment is very good.

Reading

4 Read the doctor's memo and fill in the missing information in the notice.

> **memo**
> To: Sarah Anderson
> From: Dr Parker
> Date: 10th October
>
> Please inform patients that I won't be at the surgery tomorrow morning from 9 am to noon because I have to be at a seminar. Patients can see Dr Craven if it's an emergency. Afternoon appointments are not cancelled.

1) .... October

SOUTH ROAD MEDICAL PRACTICE

2) .... will not be at the surgery today from 3) .... to 4) .... For emergencies you may see 5) .... There will be no changes to 6) .... appointments.

Vocabulary Practice

1 Fill in: *fatty foods, hard, overweight, exercise, balanced, join, stressed, long*.

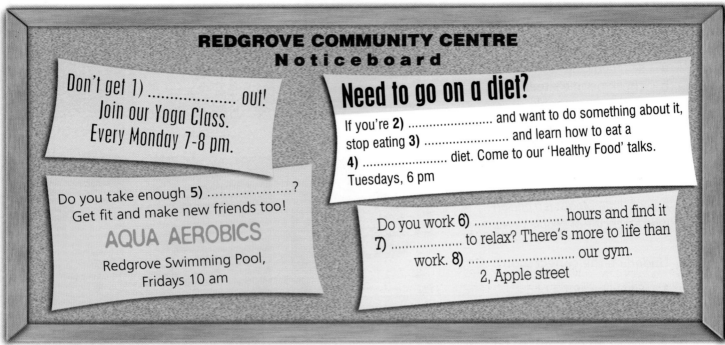

REDGROVE COMMUNITY CENTRE
N o t i c e b o a r d

Don't get 1) .... out!
Join our Yoga Class.
Every Monday 7-8 pm.

Need to go on a diet?
If you're 2) .... and want to do something about it,
stop eating 3) .... and learn how to eat a
4) .... diet. Come to our 'Healthy Food' talks.
Tuesdays, 6 pm

Do you take enough 5) ....?
Get fit and make new friends too!
AQUA AEROBICS
Redgrove Swimming Pool,
Fridays 10 am

Do you work 6) .... hours and find it
7) .... to relax? There's more to life than
work. 8) .... our gym.
2, Apple street

2 Match the words. Then, use them to complete the sentences.

put on	meals
sit	weight
take up	enough sleep
get	a new sport
drink	late
stay up	plenty of water
skip	at a desk all day

1 Kathy has .... recently. She often eats fast food.
2 Make sure you eat lunch today, Danny. It's not good to ....
3 Go to bed, Karen! You'll be sleepy tomorrow if you ....
4 Enjoy football training, Scott! Remember to .... afterwards.
5 Why don't you ...., Jason? That will help you lose weight!
6 I couldn't concentrate at school today. I didn't .... last night.
7 I love my job because I travel all the time. I really don't want to ....

Listening

3 Listen to a radio advert about a magazine and fill in the gaps (1-5).

Healthy Living
Magazine

Special 1) ....th
Birthday Edition!

The 2) ....
and our health

Special report:
low-fat foods

3) ....
and fitness

Health on
4) ....

5) £...........

46

An opinion essay

1 Read the rubric and underline the key words. What are you going to write?

> *You have had a class discussion about the following statement: 'A fast food diet is not a healthy diet'. Now your teacher has asked you to write an essay expressing your opinion and giving reasons to support it.*

2 a. Do you agree with the statement in the rubric? Why or why not? Think of two reasons to support your opinion, then read the essay to see if they are mentioned.

1▶ Do you eat fast food as one of your daily meals? Many people eat fast food for some, if not most, of their meals. However, I strongly believe that people shouldn't include so much fast food in their diets.

2▶ First of all, fast food is very high in fat, which is harmful to our bodies. For example, eating a high amount of fat makes your blood thicker. In turn, this makes it harder for your heart to pump.

3▶ Secondly, fast food diets don't contain much fresh fruit or many vegetables. Because of this, fast food does not provide people with a balanced diet. As a result, our brains and bodies do not work as well and we feel tired and stressed.

4▶ On the other hand, fast food is not so bad if people don't eat these types of meals very often. For instance, eating fast food once a week would not be considered too unhealthy. You must be careful, though, that once a week does not become once a day!

5▶ In conclusion, fast food meals are a rather unhealthy choice and lack essential nutrients, such as vitamins and minerals, that our body needs. The way I see it, people must eat different types of food to stay healthy and fit.

b. Read again and match the paragraphs (1-5) to the headings (a-e) below.

- [a] [ ] first reason & example
- [b] [ ] subject & opinion
- [c] [ ] opposing view
- [d] [ ] summary
- [e] [ ] second reason & example

3 Look at the underlined expressions in the text. Which of the expressions are used to introduce: a) opinions b) topic or supporting sentences c) an opposing view?

Your turn

4 Read the rubric. Which of the viewpoints (1-3) below agree/disagree with the statement in the rubric? Write suitable supporting sentences for each topic sentence.

> *You have had a class discussion about the following statement: 'Daily exercise is necessary for good health.' Now, your teacher has asked you to write an essay expressing your opinion and giving reasons for your views.*

1 Daily exercise is an effective way to keep a healthy weight. *When you exercise, your body burns calories faster. As a result, you won't put on extra weight.*

2 Exercise can give you more energy.
....
....
....

3 Exercise is not the only way to keep healthy.
....
....

5 Use your answers in Ex. 4 and appropriate linking words to write your essay (100-120 words). Use Ex. 2a as a model.

47

6 Grammar in Use

Conditionals Types 0 & 1

1 Use the prompts to make sentences.

1 water reach/100°C – it/boil
If water reaches 100°C, it boils.

2 you/eat lots of sweets – you/put on weight
....
....

3 you/stand on top of the building – you/ see the whole town
....
....

4 I/have a temperature – I/usually take an aspirin
....
....

5 I/not eat breakfast – I/feel weak
....

6 you/put salt in orange juice – it/taste awful
....
....

2 Look at the speech bubbles, then use the prompts to make statements, as in the example.

1 I don't want to go to the dentist. (toothache not go away)

If you don't go to the dentist, the toothache won't go away.

2 I don't want to wear glasses. (have tired eyes)

3 I don't want to take the medicine. (infection get worse)

4 I want to stay up late. (miss appointment tomorrow)

5 I eat lots of sweets and crisps. (put on weight)

6 I don't have an umbrella! (lend you mine)

3 Answer the following questions about yourself.

What will you do if you:

• get a stomach ache? • put on weight?
• catch a cold? • miss the school bus?
• wake up late?
• have a toothache?

If I get a stomach ache, I'll drink some tea.

Need(n't)/Must(n't)

4 Use *must/mustn't* to explain the signs.

① NO SMOKING
② DO NOT DROP LITTER
③ WAIT IN THE QUEUE
④ SILENCE PLEASE!
⑤ NO FOOD OR DRINK
⑥ DO NOT FEED THE ANIMALS

1 *You mustn't smoke.*

5 Complete the dietician's list of things that Laura *needs to/needn't* do to be healthy.

1 stop eating late at night
She needs to stop eating late at night.

2 avoid sweets and fatty foods
....

3 exercise all day
....

4 stop drinking orange juice
....

5 eat a balanced diet
....

6 stop eating lunch
....

48

6

6 Complete the exchanges with *needn't* or *mustn't*.

1 A: Doctor, I have a stomach ache again.
 B: From now on, you .... drink any coffee.

2 A: Nurse, I want to see the doctor right now!
 B: Sir, you .... shout in here.

3 A: I'm going to stop eating chocolate.
 B: You .... do that. Just cut down a little!

4 A: I don't want to leave you on your own.
 B: You .... worry about me. I'll be fine.

5 A: I took the tablets Steve gave me.
 B: You .... take antibiotics without a prescription!

6 A: I don't have a dress for the party. I'll buy one.
 B: You .... do that. I'll lend you one of mine.

Should/Shouldn't

7 Read the speech bubbles and give advice using the prompts and *should/shoudn't*.

I want to lose weight!

1 go on a diet
 ....
 ....

I feel tired!

2 go to bed so late
 ....
 ....

I can't study any more!

3 take a break
 ....
 ....

I've got a splitting headache!

4 drink any more coffee
 ....
 ....

I love sunbathing!

5 wear sunscreen
 ....
 ....

8 Use the words in brackets to rewrite the sentences.

1 It's not necessary to take antibiotics when you have a cold. (needn't)
 You needn't take antibiotics when you have a cold.

2 Eating lots of sweets isn't a good idea. (shouldn't)
 ....
 ....

3 Taking photos isn't allowed in the museum. (mustn't)
 ....
 ....

4 You can't go out before you finish your homework. (need to)
 ....
 ....

5 I advise you to see a doctor if the pain continues. (should)
 ....
 ....

6 It's necessary to wear a helmet when you ride a motorbike. (must)
 ....
 ....

49

1 Do you like cooking? Do you think your kitchen is safe?

2 a. Read the text quickly. Match the highlighted words to the pictures.

 b. In pairs, read the text again and complete the questionnaire.

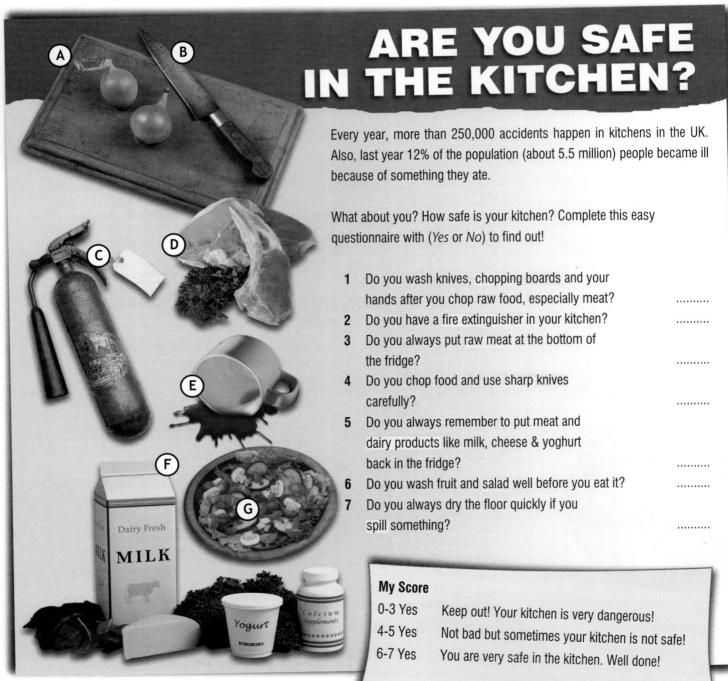

ARE YOU SAFE IN THE KITCHEN?

Every year, more than 250,000 accidents happen in kitchens in the UK. Also, last year 12% of the population (about 5.5 million) people became ill because of something they ate.

What about you? How safe is your kitchen? Complete this easy questionnaire with (*Yes* or *No*) to find out!

1 Do you wash knives, chopping boards and your hands after you chop raw food, especially meat? ....

2 Do you have a fire extinguisher in your kitchen? ....

3 Do you always put raw meat at the bottom of the fridge? ....

4 Do you chop food and use sharp knives carefully? ....

5 Do you always remember to put meat and dairy products like milk, cheese & yoghurt back in the fridge? ....

6 Do you wash fruit and salad well before you eat it? ....

7 Do you always dry the floor quickly if you spill something? ....

My Score

0-3 Yes	Keep out! Your kitchen is very dangerous!
4-5 Yes	Not bad but sometimes your kitchen is not safe!
6-7 Yes	You are very safe in the kitchen. Well done!

3 Why are the rules in the questionnaire important? Talk about your score. Is your kitchen safe?

4 Make a safety poster or leaflet for your kitchen. Use *must/mustn't*. Decorate your poster with pictures.

Progress Check

A Circle the correct item.

1 Jenny can't swallow because she has a .... throat.
   A bad   B sore   C splitting

2 Maria took a .... because she had a headache.
   A cough sweet   B painkiller
   C vitamin

3 You .... get a toothache if you eat too much sugar.
   A will   B should   C can

4 You .... worry about Maria. She'll be fine.
   A need to   B must   C needn't

5 You need to .... a dentist or else your toothache will get worse.
   A see   B go   C call

6 If you have a temperature, an aspirin usually ....
   A help   B helps   C will help

7 When I .... a cold, I usually take vitamin C.
   A have   B will have   C had

8 I'm going to the .... I need new glasses.
   A optician's   B chemist's
   C ophthalmologist

9 I feel hot. I think I have a ....
   A temperature   B cough
   C headache

10 John had a heart .... and he's still in hospital.
   A operation   B sore   C filling

11 If the pain .... worse, I will see a doctor.
   A get   B gets   C will get

12 .... meals does not help you lose weight.
   A Cutting   B Skipping   C Taking

13 You really .... to stay in bed since you have a temperature.
   A need   B must   C should

14 I often get stressed .... in this job.
   A out   B on   C in

15 You should stop eating burgers and other types of .... foods.
   A balanced   B fatty   C overweight

16 She doesn't .... enough sleep. That's why she's always tired in the morning.
   A take   B get   C make

17 It's important to drink .... of water.
   A much   B lot   C plenty

18 You .... stop smoking. It damages your health.
   A should   B can   C need

19 He .... watch so much TV. It's bad for his eyes.
   A needn't   B shouldn't   C won't

20 This body .... is excellent for sunburn.
   A cream   B painkiller   C tablets

(Marks: 20x3 / 60)

Everyday English

B Circle the correct response.

1 A: What's the matter?
   B: a I've got a terrible toothache.
      b I think I'll go to hospital.

2 A: You poor thing! You should see a doctor!
   B: a Maybe I should.
      b I've got a stomach ache.

3 A: Are you all right?
   B: a That's a good idea!
      b I'm not feeling very well.

4 A: What do you suggest I take for a cough?
   B: a Maybe I should take some syrup.
      b I suggest you take this syrup.

5 A: Can I have something for sunburn?
   B: a You can try this cream.
      b Oh dear!

(Marks: 5x8 / 40)

(Total: / 100 marks)

Vocabulary Practice

1 a. Label the pictures.

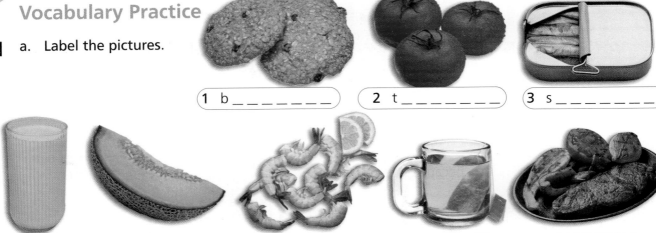

1 b _ _ _ _ _ _ _ _

2 t _ _ _ _ _ _ _ _

3 s _ _ _ _ _ _ _

4 m _ _ _

5 m _ _ _ _

6 s _ _ _ _ _ _ _

7 t _ _

8 s _ _ _ _

b. Which category does each item belong to: *fish, dairy products, seafood, vegetables, meat, drinks, snacks or fruit?* Think of three more items for each category.

2 Choose the correct word.

1 Mm, smell that! It's freshly **boiled/baked** bread!
2 I love **grilled/boiled** eggs.
3 My mother buys **steak/rice** from the butcher near our house.
4 Helen prefers fried rice to **boiled/baked**.
5 The chef recommends the **baked/roast** beef.

3 Use the words to fill in the correct headings on the menu.

• Drinks • Snacks • Appetizers
• Main Courses • Desserts

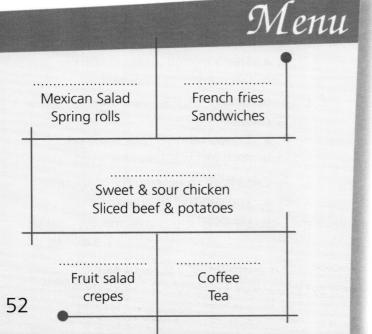

Menu

....
Mexican Salad
Spring rolls

....
French fries
Sandwiches

....
Sweet & sour chicken
Sliced beef & potatoes

....
Fruit salad
crepes

....
Coffee
Tea

Everyday English
(Ordering food at a takeaway)

4 Complete the dialogue with phrases from the list.

• It'll be there in about 20 minutes
• How can I help you
• Could I have your address and telephone number, please
• Anything else to go with that
• Is that all

A: Hello! Tom's Takeaway! **1)** ....?
B: Yes, I'd like to place an order.
A: Of course. What would you like?
B: First of all, I'd like two portions of roast beef and mashed potatoes.
A: All right. **2)** ....?
B: Um, yes, please. I'd also like two pieces of chocolate cake.
A: **3)** ....?
B: Yes.
A: OK. **4)** ....?
B: Of course. It's 14B Charlotte Street, and my phone number is 0114-7999-230.
A: ... 2 ... 3 ... 0 ... And your name, please?
B: Lori Adams.
A: All right, Ms Adams. **5)** .... Thank you for ordering from Tom's Takeaway!

Speaking

5 You are in a restaurant with your best friend and you're trying to decide what to have for dinner. Use the menu in Ex. 3 to act out dialogues.

Shopping time

Vocabulary Practice

1 Match the items in the pictures to the shops. Then, make sentences. What else can you buy in each shop?

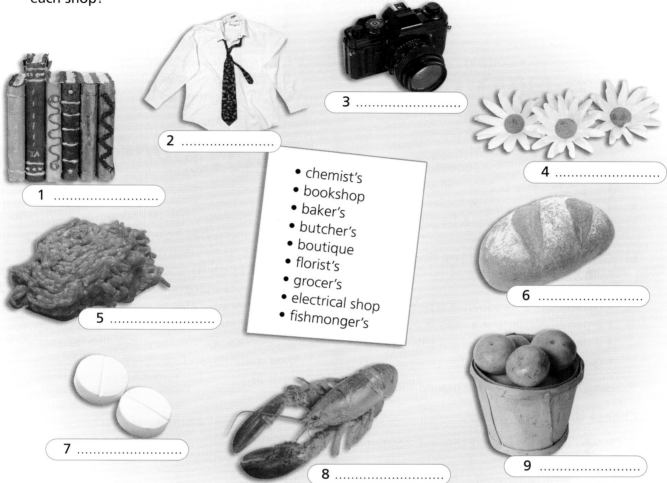

3 ....

2 ....

- chemist's
- bookshop
- baker's
- butcher's
- boutique
- florist's
- grocer's
- electrical shop
- fishmonger's

4 ....

1 ....

6 ....

5 ....

7 ....

8 ....

9 ....

You can buy books at a bookshop.

2 Circle the odd word out. What are you wearing now? Tell your partner.

1   dress, raincoat, skirt, jumper
2   jacket, anorak, uniform, coat
3   trousers, jeans, shorts, sunglasses
4   T-shirt, top, scarf, dungarees
5   handbag, ring, bracelet, earrings

I'm wearing a pair of jeans and a T-shirt.

Listening

3   Listen to the conversation and choose the correct answer (*A, B* or *C*).

1   Paula wants to buy
  A some trousers.
  B a dress.
  C a top.

2   The top Paula likes is
  A black.
  B white.
  C pink.

3   'Chic' is
  A behind the bank.
  B opposite the market.
  C next to the florist's.

4   Donna's trousers cost
  A £90.
  B £40.
  C £25.

5   Donna thinks the prices for the dresses are
  A reasonable.
  B expensive.
  C good value.

Vocabulary Practice

1 a. Complete the floor plan of a department store with the words from the list.

- health • home • games • electrical
- accessories • clothing

HARRINGTON'S DEPARTMENT STORE

5	.... & garden
4	toys & ....
3	.... goods
2	jewellery & ....
1	.... & footwear
G	.... & beauty

b. On which floor would you find the following items?

- toiletries • a handbag • a pair of jeans
- a pair of earrings • a mug • a lamp
- a pair of sandals • a chess set • a plant
- cosmetics • a discman

You would find toiletries on the ground floor.

2 Choose the correct word.

1 Helen **spends/saves** £150 on cosmetics every month.
2 Jack **lent/borrowed** his sister £50 yesterday.
3 Sir, you've forgotten your **change/cash**.
4 My cousin **earns/wins** £28,000 per year.
5 You can only pay by **cash/change**.
6 Can I **lend/borrow** your pen?

3 Fill in the correct words from the list.

- credit • salary • cash • wage • paid

A: Did you get **1)** .... today, Mary?
B: Yes I did, but unfortunately I have to pay off my **2)** .... card.
A: Oh, no! Thank goodness I don't have one. Do you use it a lot?
B: Yes, because I don't carry much **3)** .... with me.
A: I see. I want one but my weekly **4)** .... isn't as good as yours.
B: Oh well, just be patient until you've finished your training. Lawyers earn an excellent **5)** ....!

Reading

4 a. Read the text quickly and match the questions to the paragraphs.

A How much do they get?
B Do children know the value of money?
C Where do teenagers get their money?
D What about saving?
E What do they spend it on?

Money, Money, Money!

1

In the UK, two thirds of children aged 7 to 16 get pocket money **0)** *from* their parents. Sometimes, however, they have to do chores, like washing their dad's car **1)** .... mowing the lawn, to earn it. Some teenagers earn money from 'Saturday jobs' in shops, cafés or supermarkets or they have 'paper rounds' where **2)** .... deliver newspapers to people's homes. They may also get money from their parents and relatives on special occasions such **3)** .... birthdays or Christmas.

2

The average amount of pocket money from parents **4)** .... about £8.00 a week, but teenagers with jobs can earn **5)** .... lot more!

3

Kids spend a massive two thirds **6)** .... their money on snack foods such as chocolate, sweets and fizzy drinks! Boys also buy computer games, CDs and DVDs whilst girls buy clothes, shoes and toiletries such as bubble bath, perfume and makeup.

4

Apparently, only one fifth of children save, but generally, boys save better **7)** .... girls!

5

Schools now teach personal finance to all UK teenagers, so if they don't know how **8)** .... manage their money now, they soon will!

b. Read again and fill in the gaps (1-8) with the correct word.

An email describing a shopping centre

1 Read the rubric and underline the key words. Then, answer the questions.

> *Anyway, you mentioned that you went to that new shopping centre. I've heard it's great! Write and tell me what it's like!*
> *Andy*

1 Who is going to read the email?
2 What is the reason for writing?
3 What can you usually find in a shopping centre?

2 Read Geoff's email. Which of the following does he mention? Tick (✓).

- ☐ name of centre
- ☐ location
- ☐ cafés/restaurants
- ☐ opening hours
- ☐ types of shops
- ☐ outside
- ☐ hygiene
- ☐ prices
- ☐ car park(s)
- ☐ service
- ☐ décor

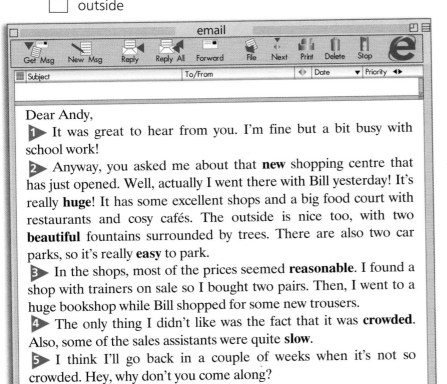

email

Get Msg | New Msg | Reply | Reply All | Forward | File | Next | Print | Delete | Stop

Subject | To/From | Date ▼ | Priority ◄►

Dear Andy,

▶1 It was great to hear from you. I'm fine but a bit busy with school work!

▶2 Anyway, you asked me about that **new** shopping centre that has just opened. Well, actually I went there with Bill yesterday! It's really **huge**! It has some excellent shops and a big food court with restaurants and cosy cafés. The outside is nice too, with two **beautiful** fountains surrounded by trees. There are also two car parks, so it's really **easy** to park.

▶3 In the shops, most of the prices seemed **reasonable**. I found a shop with trainers on sale so I bought two pairs. Then, I went to a huge bookshop while Bill shopped for some new trousers.

▶4 The only thing I didn't like was the fact that it was **crowded**. Also, some of the sales assistants were quite **slow**.

▶5 I think I'll go back in a couple of weeks when it's not so crowded. Hey, why don't you come along?

Talk to you soon,
Geoff

3 Match the paragraphs to the headings.

- a ☐ purchases and prices
- b ☐ description of shops and outside
- c ☐ opening remarks
- d ☐ closing remarks
- e ☐ opinions, service

Adjectives

4 Match the adjectives in bold in the email with their opposites.

1 difficult ≠ ....
2 old ≠ ....
3 expensive ≠ ....
4 ugly ≠ ....
5 fast ≠ ....
6 empty ≠ ....
7 tiny ≠ ....

5 Give the sentences (1-6) an opposite meaning.

1 It had a wide variety of shops.
  It had a limited variety of shops.
2 The prices were quite reasonable.
3 The shopping centre is really beautiful.
4 The shop assistants were fast and polite.
5 There was a huge car park.
6 The shops were really crowded.

Your turn

6 a. Read the rubric and complete the spidergrams.

> This is part of an email you received from your friend. *Have you been to the new department store yet? What is it like?*

b. Use your spidergrams to write an email to your friend. You can use the headings in Ex. 3 to organise your ideas into paragraphs.

Countable/Uncountable nouns – Quantifiers

1 **Put the nouns in the correct column.**

- strawberry • tea • flour • melon • biscuit
- pancake • pasta • salt • egg • bread
- cheese • potato • meat • steak • milk
- butter • lobster • honey • onion • soup

Countable	Uncountable
strawberry, ...	....
....	....
....	....
....	....

2 **Label the pictures with the nouns below. Which can go with the items in Ex.1?**

- loaf • tin • packet • jar • carton
- bottle • cup • bowl

a packet of pasta

packet   ....

....

3 **Underline the correct word.**

1 I'm very tired. I didn't get **some/any** sleep last night.
2 There are **a few/little** shops in my neighbourhood.
3 I need to go to the supermarket and buy **any/some** sugar.
4 Are there **any/some** tomatoes left in the fridge?
5 We've got **a few/little** lemons, so we can make a lemon pie.
6 There's **a few/some** bread. We don't have to go to the baker's.
7 Can I have **some/any** cherries, please?

4 **Fill in the exchanges with *some, any, a few* or *a little*.**

A: Can I have 1) .... butter on my bread?
B: There's only 2) .... left. We need to get more.

A: There aren't 3) .... bananas in the fruit bowl.
B: Look in the cupboard. I think there are 4) .... there.

A: Do we need 5) .... cheese?
B: I'm not sure. Is there 6) ...... in the fridge?

A: Are there 7) .... biscuits in the jar?
B: Only 8) .... I'll get 9) .... more when I go shopping.

Going to – Will

5 **Respond to the statements. Use the verbs in the list.**

- answer • close • tidy • wash • buy

1 It's too cold in here!   *I'll close the window.*

2 Your room is a mess!   ....

3 We haven't got any milk.   ....

4 Your clothes are dirty!   ....

5 The phone is ringing.   ....

6 Denise is going to Mexico for her holidays and has already made her plans. Write sentences, as in the example.

1 stay in the Bayview Hotel
4 sunbathe on beautiful beaches
2 try exotic drinks
5 taste local food
3 visit open markets
6 learn flamenco dancing

1   *Denise is going to stay at the Bayview Hotel.*

7 Fill in the correct form (*be going to* or *will*) of the verbs in brackets.

1   A: It's very hot in here, isn't it?
    B: Just a minute. I'*ll turn off* (**turn off**) the heating.

2   A: We haven't got any flour.
    B: I .... (**go**) and get some.

3   A: What are Sue's plans for the summer?
    B: She .... (**travel**) abroad.

4   A: Would you like me to cook something for you?
    B: No thanks! We ....
    (**have**) dinner with our parents.

5   A: Have you done the shopping yet?
    B: No, but I .... (**do**) it after work.

6   A: Why are you buying all those vegetables?
    B: Because I .... (**make**) vegetable soup.

7   A: ....
    (**you/help**) me with the shopping tomorrow?
    B: Of course.

8   A: Look at those beautiful apples.
    B: They're really fresh! I think I ....
    (**buy**) some and make an apple pie.

9   A: Why are you taking so much money with you?
    B: I .... (**pay**) the bills.

10 A: I'd like to buy that dress, but I can't afford it.
    B: I .... (**lend**) you some money.

8 Choose the correct form.

1   Sit down. I **will/I'm going to** get you something to drink.
2   The clouds are black. It **is going to/will** rain.
3   We **are going to/will** have dinner at 7. Do you want to come over?
4   Sarah **will/is going to** travel to Spain next summer.
5   I think I'**m going to/will** have the fruit salad for dessert.
6   Nancy has gone shopping; she **will/is going to** be back in an hour.
7   Do you think Andy **is going to/will** pass his exams?
8   I'm sorry I shouted at you. I'**m not going to/won't** do it again.
9   That looks heavy. I'**m going to/will** help you.
10 In the year 2100, people **are going to/will** use flying cars.

1 Look at the pictures. How are they related to the advertisment? Listen, read and check.

2 Read the text again and mark the sentences *T* (true) or *F* (false). Correct the false sentences and then, explain the words in bold.

1 Mrs Anna Blakewell first came up with the idea of afternoon tea. .....

2 Women wore special clothes for afternoon tea. .....

3 British people don't really have afternoon tea any more. .....

4 You can have lunch in Mrs Blackwell's tea room. .....

5 You can only order afternoon tea at this tea room at certain times. .....

3 Read again and make notes. Use your notes to make a summary of the text.

4 Think of a custom related to food and drink in your country and tell the class about it.

MRS BLAKEWELL'S Tea Room

Anna, seventh Duchess of Bedford, often felt hungry and tired at around four o'clock in the afternoon during the long **interval** between lunch and dinner. One day in 1840, she asked for a **tray** of tea, bread & butter and cake. It soon became fashionable for rich women to change into long gowns, gloves and hats and to **gather** in each other's houses for traditional afternoon tea. This consisted of **cucumber** sandwiches, cakes and **pastries** or scones with cream and jam. They also drank tea, of course, which they **poured** from silver pots into **delicate** china cups.

These days, afternoon tea in the average British home is more **likely** to be just a small cake or biscuit and some tea, probably made with a tea bag straight into a mug!

Our tea room has been serving lunches, snacks and traditional afternoon teas since 1912. Afternoon tea is from 3 pm to 5.30 pm daily and includes a **wide selection** of teas and **freshly-baked** cakes and scones.

OPENING HOURS:
10 am – 6 pm Mon – Sat

Mrs Blakewell's Tea Room 23a, York Road, Harrogate

Progress Check

Vocabulary & Grammar

A Circle the correct item.

1 He doesn't like meat, so he never eats ....
   A beans   B mussels   C beef

2 Could you buy me a magazine from the .... ?
   A baker's   B bookshop
   C newsagent's

3 John went to the grocer's and bought some bananas and some ....
   A pears   B envelopes
   C minced meat

4 On Sundays, I usually have .... eggs for breakfast.
   A fried   B roasted   C grilled

5 I find it difficult to eat chicken wings with a knife and ....
   A spoon   B fingers   C fork

6 I love buying accessories, especially ....
   A toiletries   B earrings   C anoraks

7 In our school, all students have to wear a ....
   A suit   B uniform   C raincoat

8 Look at those clouds! It's .... rain.
   A will   B going to   C going

9 I'm going to the .... I want to buy some plasters.
   A stationer's   B grocer's   C chemist's

10 If you pay ...., you get a 10% discount.
   A cash   B change   C credit card

11 Can I .... your sunglasses, please?
   A buy   B borrow   C lend

12 Maria .... £2000 a month as a teacher.
   A wins   B earns   C spends

13 Let's order some Chinese food from the .... near my house.
   A canteen   B coffee shop
   C takeaway

14 There isn't .... coffee left in the jar.
   A few   B some   C any

15 Would you like .... apple pie?
   A any   B some   C little

16 I think I .... go to bed early tonight.
   A am   B will   C going to

17 There isn't any milk left. I .... some.
   A 'll get   B get
   C going to get

18 Can I have a .... of bread, please?
   A tin   B loaf   C carton

19 I felt so full after the main course that I couldn't have a(n) ....
   A snack   B appetizer   C dessert

20 I'd like .... of that French cheese.
   A a little   B few   C any

$$\left(\frac{Marks:}{20 \times 3 \quad 60} \right)$$

Everyday English

B Complete the exchanges.

- what's your name
- telephone number
- you like anything
- you like
- your address and telephone number
- help you

A: Hello! Ann's takeaway. Can I **1)** ....?
B: I'd like to order some food.
A: What would **2)** ....?
B: Can I have a chicken salad and a tuna sandwich, please?
A: Would **3)** ....else?
B: No, that's all, thanks.
A: What's **4)** ....?
B: It's 2, Apple Street and the telephone number is 77778888.
A: And **5)** ....?
B: Bill Smith.
A: Thank you, Mr Smith.

$$\left(\frac{Marks:}{5 \times 8 \quad 40} \right)$$

$$\left(\frac{Total:}{100 \; marks} \right)$$

Vocabulary Practice

1 Label the pictures, then use the words below to make sentences.

- creative • boring • stressful • dangerous
- active • exciting • cheap • easy • tiring
- difficult

1 *Cycling is easy but tiring.*
2 ....
3 ....
4 ....
5 ....

1 ....
2 ....
3 ....
4 ....
5 ....

2 Rearrange the letters to form character adjectives. What hobby appears?

1 ticeva
2 ratticsi
3 srki-kitgan
4 vadsentoruu
5 eqitu
6 miagtniavie

Crossword with letters: k (1), b, x, n

1	Mary		A	classical
2	David		B	pop
3	Laura		C	jazz
4	Sarah		D	rock 'n' roll
5	Clive		E	techno
			F	rap
			G	heavy metal
			H	reggae

Listening

3 🎧 You will hear two friends talking about a music lesson. Match the people (1-5) to the types of music (A-H) they like.

Everyday English

(Expressing agreement – disagreement)

4 Fill in the gaps with the phrases below.

- Oh, I love it • So do I • I don't • Nor do I

1 A: I hate fishing.
   B: ....! It's really boring.

2 A: I can't stand jazz music.
   B: ....! It's really relaxing.

3 A: I don't like extreme sports.
   B: .... I think they're dangerous.

4 A: I really love playing music.
   B: .... It's difficult.

Vocabulary Practice

1 Match the two columns, then label the pictures.

Sports	Places
weight training	court
boxing	rink
hockey	class
badminton	room
football	field
swimming	pitch
ice-skating	ring
aerobics	course
golf	pool

1 ....

2 ....

3 ....

4 ....

5 ....

6 ....

7 ....

8 ....

9 ....

2 Find 8 items of sports equipment. Which sport(s) do we use each one for?

```
S  H  U  T  T  L  E  C  O  C  K
Y  C  D  W  N  U  J  P  G  W  V
B  C  A  A  G  O  S  O  X  E  M
I  D  H  O  O  P  G  K  X  I  E
V  S  N  K  G  G  L  Q  L  G  H
R  K  S  B  G  L  V  H  W  H  E
A  A  C  E  L  V  N  A  T  T  L
C  T  S  H  E  L  T  S  O  S  M
K  E  W  U  S  X  U  A  L  L  E
E  S  J  B  V  I  B  A  T  O  T
T  D  B  P  B  W  F  D  H  W  L
```

Speaking

3 You are going to a summer camp with a friend. Decide which are the most important things to take with you. Use the pictures to help you.

SUMMER camp 10th–17th July

Everyone Welcome! Book Now!

A: We need to take trainers for sports like football and tennis.

B: Yes, but I don't think we need…

Vocabulary Practice

1 Complete the spidergrams, then fill in the gaps in the sentences with the correct word.

> • orchestra • conductor • director
> • spotlights • western • thriller • stage
> • news • dancers • plot • chat show

documentary ← **tv** → ....

sitcom ← → ....

comedy ← **cinema** → ....

cast ← → ....

.... ← → ....

costumes

→ ....

.... ← **performance (opera, ballet, theatre, etc.)** → ....

.... ← → ....

1 Do you want to go to the cinema on Friday night? There's a really scary .... on!

2 That .... was so interesting. Whales are amazing creatures!

3 I watched a really great .... last night. The host interviewed Eddie Murphy and he was so funny!

4 Can we change channels for a minute? I just want to watch the 9 o'clock ....

5 We went to the ballet on Saturday. The .... were just incredible!

2 Look at the words and fill in adjectives that are synonyms. What type of films do these words describe?

not boring = e _ _ _ _ _ _ _
scary = f _ _ _ _ _ _ _ _ _ _
not stressful = r _ _ _ _ _ _ _
not enjoyable = d _ _ _ _ _ _ _ _ _
full of exciting surprises = d _ _ _ _ _ _ _
action-packed = t _ _ _ _ _ _ _ _

Reading

3 a. Read the title and the introduction to the text. What do you expect to read in the rest of the text? Read and check.

A visit to a musical or a circus is always a thrilling experience, but how many of you have ever thought about the hard work the performers put into these magical shows?

JAMIE SADLER, TRAPEZE ARTIST

Jamie is no ordinary teenager! He's only 14 years old, but he no longer goes to school. Instead, he's a trapeze artist with a world-famous circus!

At 10, Jamie attended a circus school for a year. Then he had an audition and joined the circus. Jamie makes swinging on a trapeze look easy, but he tells us, 'I face danger every day of my life. People ask me if I ever feel frightened when I'm up on the trapeze. Actually, I feel excited but calm!'

So what's the best thing about being in the circus? 'I love the dazzling lights, music and costumes and the way the audience gasps when I perform a difficult stunt. Also, it's fantastic afterwards when everyone is clapping and you know the performance went well.' And the worst? 'Well, it can be tiring rehearsing every day and performing at night. Also, it's difficult to be away from home when we're on tour.'

So what advice does Jamie have for others who want to become circus performers like him? 'Just don't give up!' he says with a smile. 'It was hard work to get where I am today but it was worth it! I can't think of anything else I'd rather do!'

b. Read again and mark the sentences **R** (right), **W** (wrong) or **DS** (doesn't say).

1 Jamie doesn't want to go to an ordinary school. ....

2 He doesn't really get scared. ....

3 He likes the people's reaction when he performs. ....

4 The performances always go well. ....

5 Jamie loves everything about his job. ....

6 You have to keep trying if you want to become a trapeze artist like Jamie. ....

A semi-formal letter asking for information

1 Read the rubric and underline the key words. Then answer the questions.

> You and some friends want to take a weekend break at an activity centre. Read the advertisement, then use the notes you made to write a letter to the activity centre to find out more information.

1 What kind of text are you going to write?
2 Who is going to read your piece of writing?

2 Read the advertisement. What is the purpose of it? What kind of information does it include? What else do you want to find out?

Want an action-packed Spring break?

Only £99 per person

Special early season weekend rate at

Keswick Activity Centre,
in the heart of the Lake District.

Price includes:
- mountain biking — bikes provided?
- canoeing and rafting — special equipment?
- accommodation — more info?
- food — vegetarian dishes?

All group sizes and ages catered for.

Contact us for more information or for a brochure at:
Southey Hill, Keswick, Cumbria, CA12 5NR

3 a. Look at the letter that Kevin sent to Keswick Activity Centre. Match the headings (A-E) to paragraphs (1-5).

A	Conclusion
B	Closing remarks
C	Greeting
D	Opening remarks
E	Main body

1 ☐ Dear Sir,

2 ☐ I have just read your advertisement for the activity centre in today's paper. My friends and I are interested in taking a weekend break but I would like some more information before we book.

3 ☐ Firstly, I would like to know if we need to bring anything with us. Do we need to bring our own mountain bikes or does the centre provide bikes? Could you also tell me if we have to bring any special equipment or clothing for the canoeing or rafting activities? I would also like to know what kind of accommodation is provided. Can you tell me if you provide bed sheets or if we should bring our own sleeping bags? Finally, one of my friends is a vegetarian. Do you provide vegetarian meals?

4 ☐ I look forward to hearing from you.

5 ☐ Yours faithfully,
Kevin Joyce

b. How does Kevin start/end the letter? How is this different to a letter to a friend?

4 Underline the sentences in the letter that mention the points Kevin made in his notes. What phrases does Kevin use to ask for information?

Your turn

5 Read the following advertisement, then use Kevin's notes and your answers to Ex. 4 to write sentences asking for information.

I would like to know if we need special clothing or equipment for the rock climbing.

SPECIAL WEEKEND DEALS (£79) AVAILABLE AT GANAWAY ACTIVITY CENTRE.

PRICE INCLUDES:
- Rock climbing
- Scuba diving
- Camping
- Other Sports

Phone 096-9645060 for more details.

6 Now write a letter to the activity centre asking for more information (120-150 words). Use the letter in Ex. 3a as a model.

8 Grammar in Use

Infinitive/-ing forms

1 Use the correct *infinitive* or *-ing* form of the verbs in brackets to complete the exchanges.

1 A: Do you prefer .... (swim) in a pool or in the sea?
B: Definitely in the sea.
2 A: Did she promise .... (not/tell) the secret to anyone?
B: Yes, she did.
3 A: How can you .... (do) your homework with all this noise?
B: To tell you the truth, I don't really mind.
4 A: Would you like anything else, Sir?
B: Yes, I'd like .... (order) another bottle of mineral water, please.
5 A: You look very happy. What happened?
B: I finally got the tickets for the concert! I can't wait .... (go)!
6 A: What's your favourite summer sport?
B: Well, I really enjoy .... (play) beach volleyball.
7 A: Would you like to go anywhere tonight?
B: I'd love .... (go) to the theatre!
8 A: What do you think of the green coat?
B: I hate green. I think I'll .... (buy) the red one instead.

2 Choose the correct answer (*A*, *B* or *C*).

1 I enjoy .... novels. They help me to relax.
A read   B to read   C reading
2 I apologise but you have .... out next year. I am going to sell the flat.
A to move   B move   C moving
3 Jim likes .... pizza. He can eat a whole one on his own.
A eating   B eat   C eaten
4 I'm really looking forward .... a letter from you.
A to receive   B receiving   C to receiving
5 We need .... some milk for tomorrow morning.
A buying   B buy   C to buy
6 The children can't wait for Christmas ....
A coming   B come   C to come
7 Tina likes .... to different places.
A travel   B travelling   C travelled
8 Tony would like .... Scotland someday.
A to visit   B visit   C visiting

3 Write about yourself. Use an *infinitive* or the *-ing form*.

1 I like ....
2 I can't stand ....
3 I'm good at ....
4 I'm looking forward to ....
5 I can't..................................... .
6 I just hate ....

Mustn't/Don't have to

4 Make full sentences with *mustn't/don't have to*.

1 "(You/step) on the floor! It's still wet!"
" .... "
2 "(I/wake up) early today; it's Saturday."
" .... "
3 "(You/hit) the other players."
" .... "
4 "(You/sleep) during the lesson!"
" .... "
5 "(You/bring/jacket). It's warm outside."
" .... "
6 "(Students/cheat) during the test."
" .... "
7 "(You/drive) without wearing a seat belt."
" .... "
8 "(You/touch) hot objects with bare hands."
" .... "

5 Use the phrases to tell students what they *mustn't/don't have to* do at school. You can use your own ideas.

- wear a school uniform
- buy goggles for the swimming lesson
- fall asleep in the classroom
- ask for permission to play during the break
- eat in the classroom
- bring food from home
- sing during the lesson
- write in pencil all the time
- speak with your classmates during the lesson
- damage the computers

64

6 Fill in the gaps with *mustn't* or *don't/doesn't have to*.

1 Martha .... buy a new dress. Her old one looks perfect on her.
2 Children .... play with matches. It's very dangerous.
3 You .... tell anyone, ok? It's a secret.
4 You .... shout in the library.
5 You .... bring an umbrella. It's not raining outside.
6 You .... drive carelessly.
7 It's Saturday; we .... work today!
8 You .... park your car on the pavement.

-ed & -ing participles

7 Complete the sentences with the derivatives of the words in brackets.

1 A: How was the play last night?
B: Oh, it was so .... that I almost fell asleep. **(bore)**

2 A: Are you .... about going to Paris? **(excite)**
B: Of course I am! I can't wait!

3 A: Last night's thriller was so ....! I couldn't sleep after I watched it! **(frighten)**
B: Come on, it wasn't that scary. I slept fine!

4 A: Anything .... on TV tonight? **(interest)**
B: Not much. There's a documentary about UFOs on at 9 pm.

5 A: I feel so ....! I did all the housework by myself. **(tire)**
B: Why didn't you ask me to help you?

6 A: What are you reading these days?
B: Well, as you know, I am very .... in biographies, so I am reading about Maria Callas. **(interest)**

7 A: Pauline didn't invite me to her party! I am so ....! **(surprise)**
B: She didn't? But you are best friends!

8 A: It's so dark in this room. I'm ....! **(terror)**
B: Me too! Let's try to find a candle.

8 Match the prompts in column A to the prompts in column B to form sentences.

A

1	Gabrielle felt so **tired**
2	The excursion was so **disappointing**
3	The children were so **excited**
4	They were **bored**
5	She was very **surprised**
6	I'll take these books with me on our trip
7	My feet hurt so much
8	The firework display was so **fascinating**
9	My aunt always talks about other people
10	My brother knows many things about computers

B

a because he is really **interested** in technology.
b after our **tiring** journey!
c that she went straight to bed.
d when he gave her flowers.
e that my daughter didn't want it to end.
f they were jumping up and down all day.
g because they are very **interesting**.
h that we all felt it was a waste of money.
i because her own life is so **boring**!
j because they had nothing to do.

1 Look at the picture below. Do you know this person?

Andrea Bocelli

The man with God's singing voice

Andrea Bocelli was born in September 1958 in Tuscany, Italy. His musical talent and his love for opera were easy to spot from early on. He was a natural. Andrea went blind at the age of 12. This didn't stop him from becoming one of **1)** .... opera singers in the world. In fact, it made him work **2)** .... than others. His colleagues respect him, as some things are **3)** .... for him than they are for them when on stage. Andrea has to count his steps, for example, to avoid having accidents. However, Andrea never complains and has performed for some of **4)** .... audiences on the international scene, always with **5)** .... success. Today, he has one of **6)** .... opera singer fan clubs in the world, and is popular with people of all ages.

2 Below there is a list of adjectives. Read the text and fill in the gaps with the appropriate form of the adjectives.

- difficult
- large
- famous
- demanding
- great
- hard

3 In pairs, ask and answer comprehension questions.

A: *When and where was Andrea Bocelli born?*
B: *He was born in September 1958 in Tuscany, Italy.*

4 a. Think of a person who has some kind of difficulty but still manages to live his/her life the way they want. This person could be famous or just someone you know. Make notes under the headings and use them to talk about the person.

- name
- place & date of birth
- job • achievements
- reason you admire him/her

b. Use your notes to present this person to the class.

Progress Check

Vocabulary & Grammar

A Circle the correct item.

1 Helen likes danger and she .... doing extreme sports.
A wants   B loves   C hates

2 John can't wait to .... his brother Mark.
A see   B seeing   C sees

3 Jack is a .... He plays the piano.
A teacher   B musician   C lawyer

4 I love .... arts; my favourite one is kick boxing.
A martial   B painting   C water

5 Dorothy is not .... She would never go skydiving.
A creative   B quiet   C adventurous

6 He loves plants and spends his spare time ....
A mountaineering   B gardening
C sky diving

7 Fishing is really .... Every time I do it I almost fall asleep.
A boring   B dangerous   C exciting

8 Margaret can't .... what to do.
A decide   B to decide   C deciding

9 Badminton can be a .... sport if there are two couples playing.
A team   B single   C two

10 I forgot both the .... and the ball. No table tennis for today!
A bats   B gloves   C goggles

11 Table tennis is an .... sport.
A outdoor   B indoor   C outside

12 We were sitting right next to the football ....
A court   B space   C pitch

13 The skating .... was so small that we couldn't move at all.
A rink   B court   C room

14 Pat loves her aerobic ....
A classes   B training   C play

15 Children .... swim alone in the pool. It's dangerous.
A mustn't   B don't have to
C don't need to

16 The movie was so .... and sad that I couldn't stop crying.
A depressing   B thrilling   C boring

17 You .... to wear your goggles in the pool. I only wear them because I've got an eye infection.
A mustn't   B don't have   C needn't

18 Her dress was .... It was the most beautiful dress I've ever seen.
A amazing   B nice   C good

19 The .... was very complicated and we couldn't really follow the play.
A music   B plot   C actor

20 Steven Spielberg's film won the Oscar for .... design.
A plot   B performance   C costume

$$\left(\begin{array}{c} \text{Marks:} \\ \text{20x3} \quad 60 \end{array}\right)$$

Everyday English

B Circle the correct response.

1 A: I love cycling.
B: a Nor do I.
   b So do I.

2 A: What did you think of the play?
B: a I don't, it's boring.
   b It was boring.

3 A: What was "Cats" like?
B: a It was amazing.
   b So do I. It was amazing.

4 A: Did you enjoy the film?
B: a You really have to watch it. It was fantastic.
   b I do. I find it fantastic.

5 A: I don't like fishing.
B: a I do. I find it exciting.
   b I really liked it. I find it exciting.

$$\left(\begin{array}{c} \text{Marks:} \\ \text{5x8} \quad 40 \end{array}\right)$$

$$\left(\begin{array}{c} \text{Total:} \\ \overline{\text{100 marks}} \end{array}\right)$$

Vocabulary Practice

1 Match the words in column A to the words in column B.

A	B
remote	bag
ear	pieces
black	covers
face	stand
lightweight	reception
display	control
beach	straps
clear	screen

2 Use the verbs in the list to complete the sentences.

- keep • require • plug • press
- change • view • adjust

1 If you want to play the video tape, ... the PLAY button.
2 With this Singalong microphone you can .... the lyrics of the songs on your TV screen.
3 James has moved to Dublin but we .... in touch.
4 I think these remote control cars .... batteries in order to operate.
5 Make sure you .... this cable into the DVD player.
6 Why don't we .... the channel and see if there's anything else more interesting on?
7 The TV is on too loud! Can't you .... the volume?

3 Label the pictures. Match them to their uses.

1 m _ _ _ _ _ _ _ _ _ _   2 w _ _ _ _ _ _ - t _ _ _ _ _

3 r _ _ _ _ _ c _ _ _ _ _ _ _   4 T _ _ _ _ _ _ _

5 s _ _ _ _ _ _ _ _   6 DVD p _ _ _ _ _

.... change channels	.... play DVDs
.... make sounds louder	.... communicate
.... watch TV	.... produce sound

Reading

4 **a.** **Look at the sentences below. Which ones would you see on product packaging?**

A End-of-season sale! 50% off on all electronic gadgets!
B Please do not touch!
C Special offers on gadgets on 1st floor.
D Discount on the Robosapien, the coolest personal robot!
E Batteries are not included.
F Not suitable for children under 8 years.
G Package contains 8 pieces.
H Made in China.

b. **Match statements A-H to sentences 1-5. There are three statements too many.**

1 ☐ You must buy batteries to use this gadget/toy.
2 ☐ All electronic gadgets are half-price for a period during the year.
3 ☐ You can play with this if you are over 8 years old.
4 ☐ The gadget is made up of many parts.
5 ☐ The price of the gadget is reduced.

Vocabulary Practice

1 Draw lines to match the words to the pictures. There are three extra words.

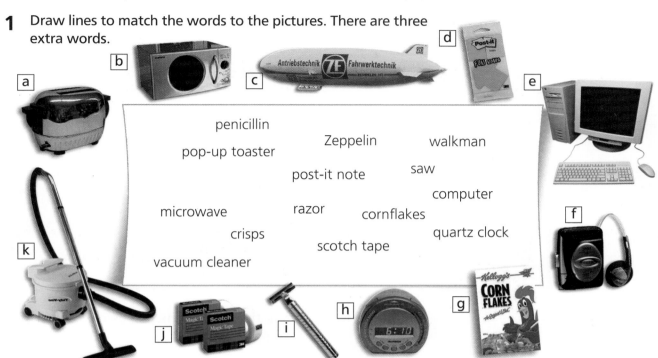

penicillin

pop-up toaster

Zeppelin   walkman

post-it note   saw

computer

microwave   razor   cornflakes

crisps   quartz clock

scotch tape

vacuum cleaner

2 a. Match the words in column A to the words in column B.

	A		B
1	fly in	a	to music
2	shave	b	a plane
3	listen	c	at eight
4	clean	d	some bread
5	write	e	dinner
6	toast	f	the beard
7	cook	g	the house
8	store	h	the information
9	stick	i	an email
10	wake up	j	(two pieces of paper) together

b. Use some of the phrases above in the correct form to complete the sentences below.

1 Let's .... to have with jam for breakfast.

2 It is safer to .... on the hard drive of the computer.

3 Why don't you use some Sellotape to .... the pages ....?

4 Have you .... yet? I'm so hungry!

5 I think you should ....; it hides your whole face.

6 I must ....; it's a mess!

Listening

3 Listen and complete the notes about a famous inventor.

The Wizard of Menlo Park

Name: Thomas Alva [0] *Edison*

Born: [1] _____, 1847

Lived: New Jersey, USA

Education: went to school for [2] _____

Invented: electric light, phonograph, motion-picture
[3] _____

Other achievements: improved telegraph and
[4] _____

Died:
[5] _____

69

Vocabulary Practice

1 **a.** Look at the leaflet below and label the pictures.

① €200

m _ _ _ _ €20

④ €430

②

③ s _ _ _ _ _ _ _

m _ _ _ _ _ _

t _ _ _ _

⑤ k _ _ _ _ _ _ _

⑥ €32

m _ _ _ _

€115

⑦ €72 s _ _ _ _ _ _

⑧ €55 p _ _ _ _ _ _

b. In pairs, ask and answer.

A: *How much is the monitor?*
B: *It's €200.*

2 Use the verbs in the list in their correct form to complete the sentences.

- send • play • surf • collect • store
- do • print • chat

1 I usually .... the Net late at night when it's cheaper.
2 She doesn't trust online shopping so she never .... it.
3 You can't really .... pictures on floppy disks; there isn't enough room.
4 Did you .... me an email yesterday? For some reason I couldn't read it.
5 If you go on this site, you'll be able to .... a lot of information on this subject.
6 Sometimes he .... online and meets some interesting people.

7 I need a copy of this letter; can you .... one for me, please?
8 Did you know that you could .... music on your computer?

3 Look at the pictures below and compare them. Think in terms of:

- what the people are doing
- where they are
- how they are feeling

Use the ideas in the box below as well as some of your own.

- school computer lab • surf the Net
- type an essay • free time • kids' sites
- under the supervision/with the help of an adult

In the first picture, the children are probably at home while in the second picture they are in the school computer lab.

Everyday English (Offering help)

4 Circle the correct response.

1 A: Can I help you to move that table?
 B: **a** I think I can manage.
 b You can, can't you?

2 A: Do you need a hand with the washing up?
 B: **a** There's no point saying that now, is there?
 b Thanks, that's really kind of you.

3 A: Shall I carry these bags for you?
 B: **a** It's ok. I'm fine, thanks.
 b Oh, dear.

4 A: Would you like me to cook dinner tonight?
 B: **a** Of course! I'm not that stupid!
 b Sure, why not!

A "for and against" essay

1 Match the topic sentences (1-4) to the supporting sentences (a-d). In pairs, add one more supporting sentence.

1 ☐ There are many advantages to sending emails instead of regular letters.
2 ☐ There are many arguments against letting young children use the Internet by themselves.
3 ☐ On the other hand, there are some drawbacks to shopping online.
4 ☐ There are many arguments in favour of using computers at school.

a The most important disadvantage is that you need to give your credit card number.
b To start with, an email takes seconds to reach the recipient.
c First of all, children find it easier to do their school projects.
d To begin with, there are many sites on the Net which are not appropriate for children.

Linkers

2 Complete the sentences with linking words/ phrases from the list. Sometimes, more than one option is correct.

• to begin with • furthermore • in addition
• on the other hand • in spite of
• for instance • in conclusion • because

1 Sitting in front of the computer for a long time can cause headaches. ...., it can hurt the eyes.
2 Surfing the Net can be very enjoyable. ...., it can be dangerous, too.
3 Many people buy things online .... the fact that it's not always safe.
4 Parents should not let their children surf the Net alone .... many sites are not safe for kids.
5 There are many advantages to working on a computer. ...., if you make a mistake, it is very easy to correct it.
6 ...., the Internet has its good and bad points.

Your turn

3 Read the introduction below. Which one of the topic sentences in Ex. 1 can be used?

> The Internet affects modern life. Indeed, it is difficult to think of life without it. However, there are also things about it we need to be careful of.

4 a. Go through the ideas below. Which of them are advantages (A) and which are disadvantages (D)?

a The Internet can be dangerous because of hackers. ......
b The Internet allows us to communicate easily, quickly and cheaply. ......
c Some people, when they surf the Net, don't know when to stop. ......
d With the Internet you are always a few mouse clicks away from any information. ......

b. Match the ideas above to the justifications/examples below.

1 ☐ You can send an email anywhere in the world at any time in seconds while a letter can take weeks.
2 ☐ They are people who can get into our computers and steal personal information or infect them with viruses.
3 ☐ They end up spending hours in front of the computer screen and don't have any other hobbies.
4 ☐ If you have a school project or if you want to buy something, you can find all you need in just a few minutes.

5 Your teacher has asked you to write an essay discussing the advantages and disadvantages of using the Internet. Use the ideas from Exs. 1, 2, and 4 to write your essay in 100-120 words.

71

Question Tags

1 Look at the pictures and complete the sentences with question tags.

She is on the phone, ...?

They look happy, ...?

You don't know how to save the document, ...?

He looked tired yesterday, ...?

You have finished the project, ...?

You haven't studied again, ...?

2 Fill in the question tags and then read the sentences aloud with the correct intonation.

sure	not sure		
✓		1	The computer crashed again, ...? ↘
	✓	2	The vacuum cleaner works, ...? ↗
✓		3	You ate all the cornflakes, ...? ↘
	✓	4	You haven't got a spare razor, ...? ↗
✓		5	John didn't fix the microwave, ...? ↘

3 Circle the correct answer.

1 You bought a new modem, **didn't / wasn't** you?
2 Maria is printing a file, **isn't / doesn't** she?
3 The file is lost now, **isn't it / doesn't** it?
4 You haven't typed your essay yet, **did / have** you?
5 The speakers work, **don't / aren't** they?

Passive Voice

4 Use the prompts to make sentences. Use the present simple passive.

1 best coffee/grow/Brazil
....
....

2 pop-up toaster/use/to make/toast
....
....

3 X-rays/use/for security/in airports
....
....

4 most computers/make/in Japan and USA
....
....

5 fastest/trains/made/the Japanese
....
....

6 best cheese/produce/France
....
....

5 Ann is back at work after a week's holiday. Her secretary didn't do what she was told to do and Ann is upset. Use the prompts and say what she is thinking, using present perfect passive.

computer/not/fix

documents/not/find

scanner/not/repair

modem/not/replace

files/not/print

6 Write sentences saying what was done and what was not done last week at Tony's office using the past simple passive.

a office clean ✗
b computer fix ✓
c keyboards clean ✓
d new monitor buy ✓
e batteries of clock replace ✓
f photos scan ✗

7 Look at the statements and make sentences using the past simple passive.

> I bought this book in Cambridge.

1 ....

> A famous Spanish poet wrote this poem.

2 ....

> I saved the file.

3 ....

> Jack fixed the computer last Monday.

4 ....

> She did not print the essay.

5 ....

8 Use the prompts and ask and answer questions using the passive.

1 Where/the best computers/produce? **(Japan)**
2 Who/penicillin/invent/by? **(Alexander Fleming)**
3 the document/save/now? **(Yes)**
4 your/phone/switch off/yesterday evening? **(No)**

9 Match the prompts and make passive sentences as in the example.

A	B	C
Brie	locate	Florida
Quartz clock	make	Leonardo da Vinci
The sauce	invent	mayonnaise and mustard
Mona Lisa	paint	France
Disneyland	produce	Jim Quartz

1 *Brie is produced in France.*
2 ....
3 ....
4 ....
5 ....

Order of Adjectives

10 Describe the objects using the adjectives.

1 plastic, black, ugly	5 green, nice, glass
2 French, nice, wooden	6 beige, rectangular, big
3 cute, old, brown	7 pink, horrible, long
4 metal, practical, white	8 yellow, attractive, plastic

1 a(n) .... chair
2 a(n) .... chair
3 a(n) .... teddy bear
4 a .... lamp
5 a .... vase
6 a .... box
7 a .... dress
8 a(n) .... telephone

73

An Inventive 150 Years

It's not easy being an inventor. Even if you do come up with a brilliant and original invention, you still have to make sure that no one else steals your idea. That is why the Patent Office exists. These are some of the inventions registered at the British Patent Office.

1901 Hubert Cecil Booth, from London, invented a machine powered by electricity which would suck up dirt. His invention was granted a patent in 1901 as the world's first vacuum cleaner.

1923 In 1923, a watch repairer from the Isle of Man, John Harwood, realised that winding watches often caused dirt to get into the mechanism. He developed the self-winding wristwatch, which had an internal mechanism and was much more accurate.

1930 One invention which helped to make the world a smaller place was the jet engine. This was invented by Sir Frank Whittle, from Coventry. His invention made travel for business and pleasure much faster and easier.

1995 In 1995, Keith Campbell and Ian Wilmut, from Edinburgh, developed an invention which people have been arguing about ever since. They invented a way to clone animals, and in 1997, Ian Wilmut cloned Dolly the sheep.

It seems that Charles H. Duell, the US Commissioner of Patents, was very wrong when he said, in 1899, "Everything that can be invented has been invented." Is there anything left to be invented? We will have to wait and see.

Vacuum cleaner

Cloned animals

Self-winding wristwatch

Jet engine

1 Look at the pictures and put them in chronological order of invention. Read and check.

2 Read again and answer the questions below.

1 What is the Patent Office?
2 What did Booth's invention do?
3 How has the jet engine helped people?
4 Which invention has caused debate?
5 Why was C.H. Duell wrong?

3 Match the words and phrases below to the highlighted words and phrases in the text.

a inside
b made better
c to make a double
d listed, recorded
e part of a machine
f (for clocks or watches) to make work by turning a key
g be given
h think of an idea or plan
i pull in
j exact, correct
k debating

4 Talk about an invention you couldn't live without. Say:

- what it is • when it was invented • what you use it for
- who it was invented by • what it does
- why you couldn't live without it

Progress Check

Vocabulary & Grammar

1 Circle the correct item.

1 The monitor is blank! Oh my goodness! The computer just .... !
   A crashed   B broke   C stopped

2 When you work on a computer, you need to .... your work every five minutes in case something happens and you lose everything.
   A save   B write   C keep

3 This is the switch off ....
   A button   B box   C stand

4 I really want to buy it! It's a .... small, round watch.
   A nice   B wooden   C green

5 I'm not going to pay €300 for an ugly .... French chair.
   A old   B vacuum   C remote

6 The .... is perfect for people who don't have time to cook.
   A microwave   B toaster
   C grill

7 The most expensive cars .... in Germany.
   A had made   B are made
   C was made

8 This house .... built in the 1940s and it is still beautiful.
   A was   B is   C were

9 The sauce .... with white wine and chicken.
   A is made   B were made
   C had made

10 .... was the vacuum cleaner invented by?
   A Who   B Whose   C Whom

11 The letters .... posted yesterday.
   A had   B were   C did

12 This novel is beautifully .... The minute you start reading it, you can't stop.
   A written   B writing   C write

13 You need a new .... This screen is awful!
   A monitor   B scanner   C keyboard

14 I want to .... the whole file but I have run out of ink. Is there another cartridge?
   A save   B write   C print

15 The .... is the main part of a computer.
   A tower   B house   C box

16 The screen is blank because you didn't switch the computer ....
   A on   B up   C off

17 She is in Paris, ... ?
   A isn't she   B doesn't she
   C won't she

18 The computer is still broken, ... ?
   A isn't it   B won't it   C wasn't it

19 You really need to shave! Don't you have money to buy a .... ?
   A razor   B walkman   C knife

20 We never call each other, we .... online.
   A talk   B speak   C chat

$$\left(\begin{matrix} \text{Marks:} & \underline{} \\ \text{20x3} & 60 \end{matrix} \right)$$

Everyday English

2 Complete the exchanges.

> • help you   • need a hand   • Would you like
> • that's really kind of you   • can manage

1 A: Can I .... to write your essay?
   B: It's ok, I'm fine.

2 A: Shall I wash the clothes for you?
   B: I think I ....

3 A: Do you .... with the ironing?
   B: Yes, please!

4 A: Can I help you to scan this document?
   B: Thanks, ...

5 A: .... me to make dinner?
   B: Sure, why not!

$$\left(\begin{matrix} \text{Marks:} & \underline{} \\ \text{5x8} & 40 \end{matrix} \right)$$

$$\left(\begin{matrix} \text{Total:} & \underline{} \\ & \text{100 marks} \end{matrix} \right)$$

75

Vocabulary Practice

1 Underline the correct word.

1 The light was moving **from/of** side to side.
2 Billy is afraid **for/of** UFO stories.
3 Many people believe **in/at** alien abductions.
4 They are very interested **for/in** UFO research.
5 Some scientists are trying to make contact **in/with** aliens.
6 Do UFOs leave traces **behind/ahead** them?
7 This book deals **from/with** unexplained mysteries.
8 Is the truth really **in/out** there?

2 Circle the odd word out.

1 comet, planet, mystery , meteor
2 space shuttle, brave , astronaut, aircraft
3 burn marks, debris, crashes, guidebooks
4 exhibition , research centre, scientist, sightings
5 unexplained mysteries, aircraft lights , lost time, alien abductions

Reading

3 **a.** Look at the title of the text. What do you think it is about? Choose from the list below, then read the first paragraph and check to see if you guessed correctly.

A a space station
B holidays in space
C NASA
D a mission to the moon

Fly Me to the Moon

Where are you going on holiday this year? The very brave and very rich can now try the ultimate adventure holiday – a trip into space! **1)** .... you got what it takes?

Tour operators such as Thomas Cook and Space Adventures are already **2)** .... bookings for holidays in space. In a recent survey, forty million Americans said that they would like to take a two-week space holiday. **3)** .... three million of them said they would be happy to pay $100,000 **4)** .... the ticket!

It sounds too expensive for most people, **5)** .... it? However, space travel doesn't have to cost the Earth. If you'd like to find out what weightlessness feels like, for $10,000, you can take a ride in 'Vomit Comet' an aeroplane run by NASA. This aircraft goes up into the sky, **6)** .... dives back down to Earth at 960km per hour – so fast that passengers really get a zero gravity experience!

Although NASA was against space tourism at first, they have changed their mind. Three members of the public have **7)** .... been space tourists, and it looks like there will soon be many more.

Don't delay! Book your ticket to space! You don't want to be left behind, do you?

b. Read the text and choose the best word (*A, B* or *C*) for each space.

1 A Has   B Have   C Had
2 A taking   B take   C taken
3 A More   B Under   C Over
4 A for   B per   C on
5 A doesn't   B don't   C does
6 A before   B then   C next
7 A yet   B still   C already

c. Would you like to take a space holiday? Discuss in pairs.

Vocabulary Practice

1 Complete the crossword.

Across

2 A type of place or house where ghosts live.
5 To think about something because you're curious about it.
6 A woman with magic powers.
8 Making a loud noise.
11 Someone who studies or researches UFOs.

Down

1 A pretty creature that looks like a small person with wings.
3 Personal things you own.
4 Someone who doubts what others believe.
7 A prediction of future events based on the stars.
9 Events that are unexplained by the laws of nature.
10 A scary creature.

2 Match the words to form phrases. Then make sentences for each.

A	B
fortune	believer
true	teller
haunted	saucer
crop	circles
flying	house

1 ....
2 ....
3 ....
4 ....
5 ....

Listening

3 (a.) Listen to the conversation and fill in the gaps (1-5).

York Ghost Walk

TAKE A WALK THROUGH THE MOST HAUNTED CITY IN EUROPE!

Walk starts: Every night at [0] 8 pm

Ends: Approx. [1] ____ pm

Meeting point: Exhibition Square (in front of the [2] ____

Haunted destinations include:

York Minster
The Treasurer's House - home of York's most famous [3] ____
'The Shambles' shopping street

Cost: Adults £3.00, students and children under 16 [4] £ ____

FOR MORE INFORMATION CALL:
[5] ____ 5609545

b. Imagine you are Sam or Amanda and you've just finished the ghost walk in York. Phone a friend and talk about what you saw and did there.

77

Vocabulary Practice

1 Fill in the blanks with the correct words from the list.

- fault • difference • climate • hesitate
- engineering • habitat • bulbs

1 If we all work together, we can make a
....

2 Don't .... to call me if you need help with the recycling campaign.

3 Some people believe that genetic .... isn't safe.

4 You can save electricity by using low-energy ....

5 Many animals are dying and losing their natural ....

6 The .... is changing and it's getting hotter and hotter.

7 I'm sorry, it's all my ....! I'm the one who crashed your car.

2 Complete the spidergram with as many environmental problems as you can think of. Compare with your partner.

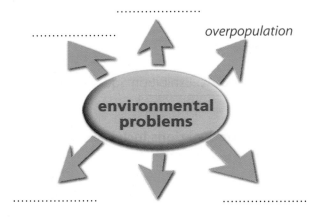

overpopulation

environmental problems

3 Match the words to their opposites. Then use them to write sentences.

A	B
filthy	help
nearby	unite
pick up	clean
war	far away
separate	drop off
harm	peace

Everyday English (Exchange Opinions)

4 Circle the correct response.

1 A: I believe everyone can help save the environment.
　B: **a** What's wrong?
　　b I agree.

2 A: The idea that genetic engineering is safe is totally wrong.
　B: **a** You're right.
　　b It's totally wrong.

3 A: As I see it, our planet is in big trouble.
　B: **a** What's the problem?
　　b You've got a point.

Speaking

5 a. Describe the photograph in pairs. Talk about:

- place • people • time • activities

b. Discuss the following questions.

1 Where do you think the woman is and why?

2 What is she holding?

3 What is the bright light behind her?

A: *In my opinion, I think that she's in a park at night.*

B: *Maybe, but she could be ...*

A story

1 What legends about scary creatures are there in your culture?

2 a. Read the story and put the paragraphs in the correct order. What scary creature is the story about?

b. Complete the gaps with the adjectives and adverbs in the list below.

- excitedly • lonely • moonlit
- spooky • cold • silver • terrified
- simply • loud • kind • old • badly

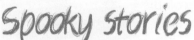

Spooky stories

[ ] She turned and ran like the wind. When she got back to the house, her granny asked: "What's wrong? You're as white as a sheet!" She described what she had heard but her granny **1)** .... laughed. Apparently, one of her neighbour's children had been out playing and had hurt herself **2)** .... Her crying was what Nora had heard. "Don't worry, Nora. The banshee won't come for me for another few years!"

[ ] The day after she arrived, Nora and her grandmother sat by the fire to talk. "Tell me a story, Granny," Nora asked **3)** .... Granny smiled and began to tell her about the banshee, an **4)** .... fairy who appeared whenever someone was about to die. "The banshee announced the death by wailing and crying while combing her grey hair with a **5)** .... comb," she continued. "Ooh Granny, that's **6)** ....!" Nora said.

[ ] It was a **7)** .... winter and Nora was visiting her grandmother in Ireland. Her grandmother was a **8)** .... and sensitive woman who knew many old stories and tales.

[ ] The next evening, Nora went for a walk along a dark, **9)** .... road. It was a **10)** .... night and she was thinking about the banshee story as she was walking along. Suddenly, she heard a **11)** .... cry in the distance. A cold shiver went down her spine. She was **12)** .... ! "That's the banshee", she thought. "Maybe she's come for my granny!"

3 *Adjectives & adverbs*, *direct speech*, *similes* and a *variety of verbs* make stories more interesting. Find examples in the text.

4 Match column A to column B, then use the similes to make sentences.

A	B
as white as	a leaf
to run like	a bee
to shake like	the wind
as busy as	night
to cry like	a baby
as black as	a sheet

John was sitting in the corner, crying like a baby.

5 Replace the adjectives in the extract below with others from the list.

- little • terrible • beautiful
- excellent • horrible

It was a **1) nice**, hot, summer morning. Laura decided to take a walk to the lake near her country house. As she was walking along the path, she suddenly saw something **2) bad**. A **3) small** bird was lying on the path with its left wing broken. It seemed to be in **4) bad** pain. She picked it up carefully and took it back to the house. Her father was a **5) good** vet; he would know what to do.

Your turn

6 Your school magazine is running a short story competition. The stories must all have the title *"A Scary Experience"*. Write a story in 120-150 words.

79

Reported Speech

1 Fill in the gaps with *say* or *tell* in the correct form or tense.

1 Nathan .... Susan that he was going to the party.
2 What did they .... you? Are they coming with us?
3 If I .... him my secret, will he promise not to let anyone know?
4 I cannot understand what you're ....
5 Mary .... me she saw you yesterday walking the dog.
6 Patrick .... to me that Vanessa was going to Spain.
7 "Oil is lighter than water," .... the teacher.
8 "I never .... you lies!" Sandra ...... Sam.
9 What do your parents .... about your new flat?
10 .... me something: is your sister's name Jenny or Jane?

2 Fill in with *said* or *told* and put the verbs in the correct tense.

1 They .... me they ....
.... (not/have) my suitcase.
2 Judy .... to us that she ....
.... (bake) a cake at the time.
3 The children .... they ....
.... (like) Disneyland.
4 The Queen .... the Prince they
.... (go) to York.
5 The fashion model .... she ....
.... (be) on a diet.
6 Melissa .... her mother she ....
.... (need) a new dress.
7 On our first day at school, my best friend
.... to me he ....
(feel) nervous.
8 The police .... that the thieves
.... (be) in prison.
9 Her father .... her yesterday he
.... (have) a surprise for her.
10 My grandparents .... they ....
.... (want) me to go with them to Brazil.

3 Karen, a famous model, gave an interview two months ago. Read the answers she gave and then change them into *reported speech*.

1 I'm working in London at the moment.
2 Unfortunately, I don't have any pets.
3 I don't eat chocolate or white bread.
4 I really enjoy going out with friends!
5 I don't like light colours at all.
6 I love going to the cinema and watching comedies.
7 I hate spiders!
8 I am afraid of heights.

Karen said (that) ...
Karen told the reporter (that) ...

Relative Pronouns

4 Link the pairs of sentences using *who*, *which*, *that*, *whose*.

1 Rachel is talking to a woman. The woman looks angry.
....
2 I live in a cottage. The cottage is at the top of a hill.
....
3 Simon got a cat. The cat's name is Nicole.
....
4 My brother bought a leather jacket. The colour of the jacket is black.
....
5 I work in Sydney. Sydney is a beautiful city.
....
6 The zoo is full of animals. The animals' cages are very dirty.
....
7 This is a great football team. The team has won many championships.
....

8 Did you see that light? That light came from the sky!
....

9 My sister has two daughters. Their names are Jemma and Jackie.
....

10 The children are playing with a woman. The woman is holding a balloon.
....

5 Some new people have moved into Sally's neighbourhood. Sally is throwing a welcoming party for them. Introduce them to the rest of the neighbours. Use *who* or *whose*.

Sophie/student from France

Luke/his sister/nurse

Alice/her son/three years old

Carol/expect/baby

Mrs Johnson/English teacher

Geoff/his business/go very well

Dr Bakshi/work/local hospital

Mr Thompson/Carol's husband

Reported Questions/ Commands

6 Rewrite the following questions in *reported speech*.

1 Can you swim?
He asked ....

2 Where do you live?
She asked ....

3 Are you enjoying the party?
They asked ....

4 How can I help you?
She asked ....

5 Why are you crying?
She asked ....

6 Do you like playing tennis?
He asked ....

7 Does Emma study hard?
She asked ....

8 When do you meet your friends?
He asked ....

7 Turn the following sentences into *reported speech*, as in the example.

1 1 *The teacher told us not to waste electricity.*
2 Recycle!
3 Don't throw away plastic bottles!
4 Walk to school!
5 Use less water!
6 Use public transport!
7 Don't drop litter!
8 Buy organic products!

1 *The teacher told us not to waste electricity.*
2 ....
3 ....
4 ....
5 ....
6 ....
7 ....
8 ....

81

Sun · Jupiter · Saturn · Uranus · Neptune · Pluto & Charon · Mercury · Venus · Earth · Mars

1 Look at the picture. What are the planets called in your language? How can the picture be related to the text?

2 a. Now look at the headings in the text. What do you think you are going to read in each section? Read and check.

b. Read again and mark the statements **Y** (yes) or **N** (no).

1 NASA was formed in the 20th century. ....
2 The first moon walk was in 1961. ....
3 Only astronauts from the USA work on the ISS. ....
4 Astronauts work most of the day. ....
5 There is no gravity on the ISS. ....
6 It would take two months to reach Mars. ....

c. Which events are related to the years listed?

• 2000 • 1969 • 2019 • 1958 • 1961

3 Imagine you are a NASA representative being interviewed. In pairs, take roles and act out the interview. Use the text for information.

How it all began

On 1st October, 1958 the National Aeronautics and Space Administration (or NASA) was created by the US government. In 1961, Alan Shepherd became the first American astronaut to fly into space. NASA's greatest achievement, however, was on 20th July, 1969, when Neil Armstrong became the first person to walk on the moon.

NASA's Mission

NASA's original aim was to develop America's space programme, but it does much more than that. NASA Administrator, Sean O'Keefe, claims that they want to do what has never been done before, and that their mission is: "To understand and protect our home planet; to explore the universe and search for life; to inspire the next generation of explorers ... as only NASA can."

The International Space Station (ISS)

The International Space Station has been home to NASA astronauts, as well as astronauts from Russia, Canada, Japan, France and Italy, since November 2000. The astronauts carry out scientific research and work on the space station itself. They have free time to cook, read and play games, just like they would have on Earth. The only problem is that they have to do all these things without gravity!

Mission to Mars

NASA has wanted to put an astronaut on Mars for many years. However, this is much more difficult than sending a man to the Moon. First of all, Mars is much further away, and it would take between 100 and 250 days to get there. Also, Mars has much stronger gravity, so it is hard to land and take off again. Despite these problems, NASA has already sent unmanned missions to Mars and they are determined that by 2019, man will walk on the 'Red Planet'.

Progress Check

Vocabulary & Grammar

A Circle the correct item.

1 Most people do not believe that .... exist.
A aliens   B stars   C satellites

2 The Sun is not the only star in our .... system.
A solar   B moon   C Earth

3 Venus is a .... just like Earth.
A planet   B comet   C star

4 Nowadays, we can watch television from any part of the world via ....
A moon   B satellite   C spaceship

5 Maria .... us that she works for NASA.
A said   B told   C spoke

6 "The UFO landed on the roof of my house," he ....
A said   B told   C spoke

7 He told her that he .... tired.
A was   B does   C is

8 We shouldn't enter this house. It is ....:....!
A haunted   B hunting   C hunt

9 In fairy tales, ... are always ugly and fly on brooms.
A witches   B fairies   C heroines

10 Maria is the girl .... believes in ghosts.
A who   B which   C whose

11 Ann is the girl .... mother is a singer.
A which   B whose   C that

12 John is the boy .... car is blue.
A who   B which   C whose

13 This is the house .... looks like a spaceship.
A which   B whose   C who

14 Chinese couples must have only one child because of ....
A deforestation   B overpopulation   C pollution

15 Every year, it's getting hotter and hotter because the .... is changing.
A climate   B pollution   C earth

16 Ann .... me where John was.
A tell   B told   C said

17 The science that changes the genes of plants and animals is called genetic ....
A engineering   B biology
C medicine

18 .... of water, oil and metals is due to wasting Earth's natural resources.
A Depletion   B Pollution
C Deforestation

19 You should .... your newspapers. Don't just throw them away.
A renew   B recycle   C reward

20 I could hear a terrible .... sound coming from the old house.
A haunted   B solar   C howling

Everyday English

$\left(\text{Marks:} \dfrac{\quad}{60} \; 20\times3 \right)$

B Fill in the gaps using the prompts and then match sentences 1-5 to the responses (a-e).

- There's this • The idea • I strongly
- As I see it • In my opinion

1 .... aliens do not exist.

2 .... theory that aliens are living here on Earth.

3 .... that aliens are green comes from the movies.

4 .... believe that we should all recycle.

5 ...., the Amazon forests will soon disappear.

- I see • That's • You are • You've got
- I suppose you

a .... true. The forests are slowly disappearing.

b .... right. Recycling is very important.

c ....a point there. Aliens are always green in films!

d .... are right, but many people do believe in aliens.

e .... what you mean. But how is that possible?

$\left(\text{Marks:} \dfrac{\quad}{40} \; 5\times8 \right)$

$\left(\text{Total:} \dfrac{\quad}{100 \text{ marks}} \right)$

Irregular Verbs

Infinitive	Past	Past Participle	Infinitive	Past	Past Participle
be	was	been	lie	lay	lain
bear	bore	born(e)	light	lit	lit
beat	beat	beaten	lose	lost	lost
become	became	become	make	made	made
begin	began	begun	mean	meant	meant
bite	bit	bitten	meet	met	met
blow	blew	blown	pay	paid	paid
break	broke	broken	put	put	put
bring	brought	brought	read	read	read
build	built	built	ride	rode	ridden
burn	burnt (burned)	burnt (burned)	ring	rang	rung
burst	burst	burst	rise	rose	risen
buy	bought	bought	run	ran	run
can	could	(been able to)	say	said	said
catch	caught	caught	see	saw	seen
choose	chose	chosen	seek	sought	sought
come	came	come	sell	sold	sold
cost	cost	cost	send	sent	sent
cut	cut	cut	set	set	set
deal	dealt	dealt	sew	sewed	sewn
dig	dug	dug	shake	shook	shaken
do	did	done	shine	shone	shone
dream	dreamt (dreamed)	dreamt (dreamed)	shoot	shot	shot
drink	drank	drunk	show	showed	shown
drive	drove	driven	shut	shut	shut
eat	ate	eaten	sing	sang	sung
fall	fell	fallen	sit	sat	sat
feed	fed	fed	sleep	slept	slept
feel	felt	felt	smell	smelt (smelled)	smelt (smelled)
fight	fought	fought	speak	spoke	spoken
find	found	found	spell	spelt (spelled)	spelt (spelled)
flee	fled	fled	spend	spent	spent
fly	flew	flown	split	split	split
forbid	forbade	forbidden	spread	spread	spread
forget	forgot	forgotten	spring	sprang	sprung
forgive	forgave	forgiven	stand	stood	stood
freeze	froze	frozen	steal	stole	stolen
get	got	got	stick	stuck	stuck
give	gave	given	sting	stung	stung
go	went	gone	stink	stank	stunk
grow	grew	grown	strike	struck	struck
hang	hung (hanged)	hung (hanged)	swear	swore	sworn
have	had	had	sweep	swept	swept
hear	heard	heard	swim	swam	swum
hide	hid	hidden	take	took	taken
hit	hit	hit	teach	taught	taught
hold	held	held	tear	tore	torn
hurt	hurt	hurt	tell	told	told
keep	kept	kept	think	thought	thought
know	knew	known	throw	threw	thrown
lay	laid	laid	understand	understood	understood
lead	led	led	wake	woke	woken
learn	learnt (learned)	learnt (learned)	wear	wore	worn
leave	left	left	win	won	won
lend	lent	lent	write	wrote	written
let	let	let			

Projects

A story

Project 1

Look at the picture. Then write your story entitled "Problem solved" for the school magazine's annual short story competition. (120-180 words)

Problem SOLVED

....
....
....
....
....
....
....
....
....
....
....
....
....
....
....
....
....
....
....
....

A poster:
Rainforests

Collect information then make a poster about rainforests. Present it to the class.

Rainforests

What is a rainforest?

....
....
....
....
....

Where are rainforests located?

....
....
....
....
....

What plants are there in rainforests?

....
....
....
....
....

What animals live in rainforests?

....
....
....
....
....

What is the weather like in rainforests?

....
....
....
....
....

A class survey:
how teenagers spend their money

1 Work in groups. Think of five questions you can ask your classmates about what they spend their money on. Make a questionnaire like this, photocopy it and give it to your classmates to complete.

Survey: spending money

Name: ....   **Age:** ....   **Sex:** ....

1 Where do you get most of your money?
- part-time jobs (e.g. babysitting, raking leaves, etc)   ....
- allowance   ....
- gifts   ....
- other (give details)   ....

2 How much money do you get a week?
....
....

3 How much do you spend on ...
going out? ....
CDs/videos? ....

---

2 Put all the answers together. Use the questions to write your report.

Where do you get most of your money?
Most of my classmates ....